Yorkshire's FARM LIFE

compiled by **David Joy**

Dalesman Publishing Company Limited,
Stable Courtyard, Broughton Hall,
Skipton, North Yorkshire BD23 3AE

First Published 1994

Cover: Walter Walker of Appletreewick by Geoff Lund

Typeset by Lands Services
Printed by The Grange Press

A British Library Cataloguing in Publication
record is available for this book

ISBN 1 85568 069 6

There are three ways of losing money;
Backing horses is the quickest,
Wine and women is the pleasantest,
But fattening bullocks is the surest.

When the cuckoo sings on an empty bough
Keep your hay and sell your cow.

Old Yorkshire sayings

Contents

List of Illustrations

Foreword

Reading through past volumes of the *Dalesman* to compile *Yorkshire's Farm Life* has been a very special pleasure. Perhaps it is because I come from Dales farming stock. Most of my ancestors have toiled in conditions often harsh in the extreme, daily doing battle with a hostile climate, stubborn ewes and dismal peat fires on the upland edge of Wharfedale.

Indeed, two of them feature in these pages. There is Shepherd Thomas Joy, who spent a lifetime tending flocks on Grassington Moor and came to know every inch of its vast emptiness. And there is Farmer Anthony Joy, my great uncle, noted for his "kindly welcome and merry twinkle in his eyes". He had an inherent love of the Dales, refused to acknowledge summer time and was so fond of animals that it was difficult to keep sheep out of the house!

Yorkshire's farming folk are not easy to get to know. They have been described as bloody-minded and a race apart, although often these characteristics stem from an inherent shyness and suspicion of strangers. The prolific writer J. Fairfax-Blakeborough gives a fairer assessment in the closing extract in this book, when he refers to people "a bit slower of thought and movement, more conservative, content with simpler things but made up of robust men and women, with brawn and muscle, sturdy, staid and dependent, proud and independent".

We all tend to glamourise the past, and thus it is inevitable that the following pages look back at what is perceived as a golden age. The continuous rain, acres of mud and absence of mechanical aids tend to be forgotten and change is lamented: "The loneliness of the fields, the absence of the bands of workers, of their music, laughter and banter – the soul seems to have been dragged out of it all."

Yet change had to come. Spending half a day trailing up to a remote hillside barn, milking a few cows by hand in near darkness, mucking out through the forking hole and then lugging a can back to the dairy was a way of life that belonged to the stone age. Yorkshire's farm life in the 1990s bears little relation to that recalled in these pages, but it is still possible for a farmer to lean over a gate at the end of a long and hard day, watch the harvest moon rising over his own acres and feel an immense sense of well-being and satisfaction.

David Joy
Editor, The Dalesman, *1988-1993*

Farming Ways

Farm life in Bishopdale

I remember the day I first came here in May nearly twenty years ago, when I thought it was the most beautiful valley I had ever seen. Nor have I found reason to change my mind. Snow still lay in hollows on the tops of the fells, over which the curlews wheeled, uttering their wild, bubbling, spring-time call, and the beck foamed along the valley bottom.

I often used to walk past our farmhouse in those days, but no inner voice whispered that one day I would live there myself. My husband also, often came walking down this dale as a young man, but he never knew that one day he would be a farmer and live in the house across the stepping-stones.

In actual fact the farm was started soon after the school, to supply the children with tuberculin tested milk and teach them all about farming. The school broke up at the end of the war but we remained, and though the gooseberries no longer disappeared from the garden, we missed our merry helpers.

It did not take very long to get in a field of hay in those days. The children used to rake up the field in a long line and when they arrived at the top they turned and raked down the field again. James, our musical prodigy, once got to the top and then proceeded up the hillside raking nothing at all for a good five minutes, while we leaned on our rakes to see how long it would take him to emerge from the entrancement of musical composition.

Oh, happy brown-legged children, so far from the sight and

sound of war! Now they are scattered, but they all remember Bishopdale with love and longing.

We have lived here long enough to witness the decay of the old era and the dawn of the new age. Electricity is coming up the dale at last, and the road is being widened to meet the needs of the heavy holiday traffic. I am saddened at the passing of the secret, hidden places that used to lie so far from life's fitful fever. I shall have to hie me to Himalaya or a remote Canadian forest if the dales become too civilised.

We never saw the scythe in sole use at hay-time. It is only used now for those odd little corners that machines cannot get at, but when we came to Bishopdale during the war tractors were unknown and all the old horse-drawn machines were in use. They were just like my grandfather's hay-making implements on the little farm in Nova Scotia where I was born.

In my childhood days the golden wagon loads were drawn by Prince to a great covered barn, where the hay would be well protected from the snows. You could take your time about hay-making in Canada, for the summers were hot. Up here in the high dales quick methods of hay-making have had to be evolved because of the heavy rainfall.

Almost every field contains its own grey stone barn with a hay loft above and byres below. On very fine days when the hay makes quickly, it is rowed up by a win-rower and then swept directly to the barn, where it is forked up without further ado.

On more unsettled days the hay is often made into small cocks and from these forked up into big pikes which can stand up to a good deal of rain if they are well made. The pikes can be transferred to the barns at leisure when the weather improves.

Excepting for the remarkable summer of 1955, the last few hay-times have hardly seen a dry day up in these hills. We shiver in barns over the mugs of tea and cakes I bring out to refresh the tired men, and my husband drives the tractor well muffled in thick pullovers and scarves. If a fine day comes one might be lucky enough to get hold of that popular man, the baler. How exciting that is!

The baling machine goes round and round the field, licking up hay at one end and spitting it out in neatly tied bales at the other. Everyone turns out to help or watch, and the cats all come to play leap-frog over the bales. For a few hours the hayfield looks more like its old cheerful self of the days when summers were summers.

We have made much of our hay on tripods during the past few years, because by this method it can be put on half-green. Unless a howling gale sweeps down the dale blowing all the tripods over, very fine hay is made in this way.

One certainly tries every possible way of fooling the weather, including silage-making, but nevertheless during some years lately we have not finished dealing with the hay-crop till the beginning of October. At least we can be thankful that it has all been gathered in – no rotting grass or pikes floating in the floods.

Because we tend to glamourise the past in retrospect, I know that in after years I shall gloss over the continuous rain and the acres of mud. I shall best remember our dale on a perfect summer evening, as a sort of earthly Paradise, a Shangri-La set in the English hills. My husband is standing beneath the damson tree playing his violin while his faithful hound lies at his feet.

She sleeps warily with one ear cocked and one eye on her traditional enemies the cats, who are scatting madly round and round the garden. Lambkin is standing on the wall pruning roses, tiger lilies, any herbage within reach, excepting mere commonplace grass.

The children run past the house twirling their bathing costumes, off for a last swim in the beck before bed-time. They will not need a bath tonight but they will be very hungry indeed for good milk and home-made wholemeal bread. No wonder they look so healthy.

The pleasure traffic has returned to the great industrial towns, leaving the dale to the dwellers therein, while over the hill the risen moon starts to brighten and the first owl calls softly. That is how I shall remember it all. But, as I sit outside the shooting-box, I wonder where it will all end, this new age we are coming to.

Will the soil be heated by atomic power, thus releasing its marvellous fertility? Will there be summer chalets and helicopters all over the fells? Shall we be shepherding the sheep by radar?

Who knows – but I hope I shall not be here to see.

Elizabeth Large (1959)

Different Ways

"A lot of these low-country farmers don't know they're born," remarked a dalesman in August when he looked out of the bus window and saw the corn harvest well on the way.

"They're a month ahead of us," said his companion, "and they haven't to scow on't hill-sides like we have."

"And another thing," broke in a hill farmer on the seat in front. "We have two harvests they know nowt about down here in England. There's peat ti cut an' lead, and there's bracken ti scythe and set into stack. We've got both. It's a bit since we greeaved any peat, but I said we wouldn't be caught this winter like we were t'winter afore last."

The first speaker added, "We've getten a useful stack o' turrves an' all. Bracken gets ranker with us. There'd be a vast more good grazing for t'sheep if we could get rid of it. It's not stuff I like much for bedding, although we use a lot. They say it isn't worth much on t'land, but I argues that aught what rots maks manure... We've been a bit earlier with harvest this year and I've seen some goodish crops in the high country – field of oats what'll tak' a bit o' beating on any of these low-country farms. But ours isn't really a corn country and it's daftness ploughing out good grass to grow wheat when it's allus a gammell that it'll be harvested in any sort of condition."

One of the other hill farmers then said, "These low-country farmers don't understand how we go on and what we have ti' contend wi'. It needs a man wi' a lot more brains and contrivance ti' make ends meet on the moors, than it does down here in England."

J. Fairfax-Blakeborough (1948)

The Day we needed a Sled

There came a day when one of my wife's in-calf heifers scaled a drystone wall and fell down into a whin-grown hollow below the old quarry on our North Yorkshire moor-bank field. There among the broken stone she "gat kessen" as soon as, or perhaps before, the onset of labour. Anyhow, when my wife found her, the calf was dead, but luckily its face and forefeet were clear.

My wife telephoned the vet: she is always telephoning vets. Considering it was Sunday morning he arrived with remarkable dispatch, summoned by his private radio network. We took him as near the scene of action as a Land Rover would get – a long field away.

After a brisk uphill walk he took in the situation at a glance. All the resources of modern science came into play. He put a rope's end in our hands and said "Heave." It was a bull calf, and seemed huge. Why do the dead one's always seem so much bigger? The heifer seemed exhausted but not otherwise ailing. She might, said the vet, take anything up to 24 hours before she was strong enough to walk.

Meanwhile, she must be fed, and given drinks. Four meals a day, which had to be transported by Himalayan porterage, likewise the blankets, sacks and New Zealand rugs to ward off pneumonia. Four times every 24 hours. Hay, mash, and a disgusting posset compounded of dried milk and black treacle which she slurped down with relish. At dusk, and midnight, before sunrise and at noon.

Although she could not be induced to move the way we wanted, every time we visited her she had struggled far enough to throw off the waterproof coverings. But always without loss of appetite. It was quite simply a race. Would she recover the strength and the will to walk before pneumonia or mastitis or both set in? If she was down in the byre we could put another calf on her and that would lessen the mastitis risk.

Noon on Monday found her still eating, still immobile, and the weather worsening. Somehow we must get her down the hill. We did in fact get her to her feet, but always her left hind leg collapsed under her as she stepped forward with the others. Evidently some damage to the pelvic nerve caused by the difficult labour, for there was no sign of fracture or dislocation. Such damage sometimes heals of itself, under the right conditions, which means in the byre.

Short of walking or a helicopter there was no way to the byre. It was like one of those practical problems they used to set the syndicates at O.C.T.U. Only there were six of us in the syndicate, all under 25. Now there were two of us, and speaking for myself, the wrong side of 50. She lay now on the rim of a rocky cup, above a whin-covered brow. There seemed nothing to lose. We rolled her down the brow, on to the flatter, softer, and also wetter ground, perhaps 50 yards nearer home.

"What you want," said the Good Neighbour, "is a sled. I used to see a lot about." So did I, 30 years back, on moor-end farms, leading hay and scaling muck. "Never see them now. Thing of the past."

Yes, indeed.

"Think on though," he added, "I know a chap has one yet. At Grosmont. I'll let you know."

On Tuesday in the early afternoon, a tractor drew up panting and stinking, outside our gate, driven by the Chap. From the very latest pattern of trailer he unloaded the most antique, his sled. It had a rim like a saucer, and the final primitive touch was added by the runners, which were of half-round green wood, straight from the bough. The tractor sailed up the sodden fields, past the welter of skidmarks where the Land Rover had given up the struggle, through a gap in the wall and into the hollow where the heifer lay, once again unwrapped. The Chap was resourceful, methodical, and skilled with ropes. The heifer weighed some nine hundredweight, and the three of us could not lift her.

He unhitched the sled, tilted it, and scooped her up with its saucer-like rim, then lashed her down. The low-loading horse ambulance costing thousands of pounds that they use to pick up racehorse casualties could not have got within a furlong of her on that slope over that sodden clay.

In half an hour she was in the byre – home, as they say, and dry – while the icy rain lashed down over Eskdale.

But as I was saying, the sled is a thing of the past...

A.A. Dent (1969)

Farming Tradition

Four tups, who have been keeping company this last week or more with three young pigs in the croft across the road below my window, were taken away this morning to join the doubtless more congenial company of a flock of breeding ewes: their place was taken by a cart-horse. A very simple operation – the most common-place incident of farming life – yet, for all I've seen the same sort of thing many a time before, a minor miracle of deft performance by man and dog.

The sheep were right away at the far end of the croft: man and horse on the road this end: the pigs rooting in mid-field. The man opened the gate and the horse, encouraged by a light smack from its discarded halter, trotted through.

For a moment I thought that was all, but, instead of closing the gate again, the man gave a low whistle and the dog, which till then I had scarcely noticed, streaked away across the field. Half-way across he saw the pigs and checked, swinging round as if to ask his master whether it could be these queer looking animals that he wanted gathered. But the whistle was repeated and the dog immediately swung back and ran on till he was beyond the sheep – another different whistle and the sheep were lolloping fast, but without alarm, towards the gate – nearing it and the man, they turned off to one side – yet another whistle and the dog had swung out beyond them... For a second or two the sheep stood still (were they wondering how to escape? probably; but they might just as well be wondering which way man and dog wanted them to go; their alert but blank faces gave me no hint of their motives) – then a final whistle and the sheep turned and trotted on, in obedient unconcern, straight out between man and gate into the road. Up came another man with the ewes; the tups joined the flock; the dog and man fell to the rear; and the procession passed on through the village and out of sight.

The whole process took something under two minutes; but what a two minutes' worth of farming tradition! – of unerring skill built up through countless generations of breeding and discipline.

Now this evening I've just looked out at the croft again. The horse has gone and – why, I don't know – the tups have returned, grazing on in placid unconcern as if they had never had a holiday at all. But as I watched them, the thirteen-year-old "bright boy" of the village came by, stick in hand, driving before him three little girls for all the world as if they were a flock of sheep. Just like the man's this morning were his side-stepping gait and his "shooing" movements of arm and stick, and he even whistled to an imaginary dog to help him. So the tradition goes on... I must add that the little girls didn't behave in the least like sheep; after noisy expostulation, they quickly evaded their driver and ran merrily back down the road, leaving him alone.

John Dower (1941)

The Day we moved Nimbus

I don't think Nimbus had ever been out of the yard since the day he was born. And that was a good few years ago. He was a great big fellow now and quiet enough when kept to his routine. He could put an evil glint in his eye if he had a mind to and he took a delight in making such a to-do in his box as to get you out of bed in the night. But I never knew him to make more damage than an odd splintered rail and once he broke the water pipe to his drinking bowl. He never went for a man, which is more than I can say for the others.

No, Nimbus was all right if you let him alone. I'd say he was the quietest of the lot, considering his age. I suppose that's why the gov'nor picked on him.

It's no more than twenty minutes walk to Newbank farm if you cut across the back pasture and below the edge of the wood. It's a well worn track, for one of us has to go over every other Sunday to do relief when Tom has his weekend off. But it's not a path you could lead a bull along. At least not an eight year old Jersey that has never even seen the other side of the drift-house gate. So he had to travel by road, which is a good three miles and passes by the Plough and the bakers.

It's nothing new to us to be taking a beast by road. Almost every month we are moving stuff up to the sales. With nearly 200 head milking between the two farms we have a fair take-off. It seems funny to think of it now, but up till the time we moved old Nimbus I'd never shipped a bull in the twelve years I'd been at Gale End. Perhaps you might say the whole thing was lack of experience.

The day we moved Nimbus we had the car and trailer laid on straight after breakfast. Jim had got it nicely backed up to the drift-house gate and there was a whole turn out to see the fun. We'd had him tied up since his early morning feed so's he'd get used to the feel of the rope. He was used to the slip chain and sometimes the pole, but a rope across his face and behind his ears was something new for him. He didn't seem to mind too much, but all the same I put a sack across his eyes while we got him in. Of course he made a bit of a shy when his weight tipped the tail-board as he stepped on it, but even heifers do that. It is a bit of a surprise to any beast when the while thing rocks and clatters on the drawbar hitch.

The trailer was none too big for him; he could no more than raise his head a couple of neck creases without scraping the roof and it took four of us to shut the tail-board up against his back side. Well, he stood quiet enough inside so I tied him slack to the side and off we set.

If I'd been on my own I might say that perhaps I'd been mistaken, but there was Jim with me all the way, for he was driving. He'll tell you the same; that bull never made so much as a shudder. It was as though we didn't have anything in the trailer at all. It was so rum that just before we turned into the main road I said to Jim we'd better have a look.

There are slatted sides to that trailer so I could see inside a bit without taking the tail-board down. He seemed to be all right, not making a muff, still tied up and rolling his old eyes round at me like he always does, Then it just struck me and I said to Jim how I thought he seemed to be a mite lower down than he should be. I thought maybe he'd got down on his knees. Well, it seemed a bit of a puzzle but he looked happy enough and I reckoned we'd better move on.

Of course, Jim is always thinking of the mechanical side and he got down to look at the brake cables or something while I was getting back into the car. Then he let out such a yip and yelled come and look quick. He was on his belly on the road staring under the trailer so I got down and had a look too. Look at them feet, said Jim.

There they were, four of them all right. They were Nimbus's, there was no mistake about that. All were planted firmly on the ground. I said to Jim, "That's why he's standing so low." Jim replied, "I wonder how far he's been running."

We undid the tail-board to get a closer look. There was hardly a scrap of that trailer floor left – just a few splinters at either end, and old Nimbus standing astride the axle. There wasn't a mark on him though. It must have given way steadily and he must have treaded it off as it hit the ground. He was blowing a bit, I could see now, but it's best part of a mile to the turn off and Jim doesn't drive too slowly.

Jim said we'd have to make a plan of action. He's always using these kind of sayings because he was in the Army. I said we'd better get down to doing something, as Nimbus wasn't used to being planned about. If he wasn't made a bit more comfortable presently he might take it into his head to bash up the whole trailer.

The first thing that struck me was that we dare not let the old devil out. There would be no telling what he would do and neither Jim nor me would stand any chance of holding him. At the same time we couldn't carry on as we were, even though he didn't seem to have managed too badly galloping along inside the trailer. So it seemed we'd have to mend it.

It didn't take long to find some materials, for Mrs. Jones was standing at her gate watching us and she hollered out to ask what was to do. Mrs. Jones is a very practical kind of woman and she soon came along to have a look. She said that we'd want a new trailer floor all right and then she slipped off without a word and came bustling back with her old man's foot rule. "Here, get in and measure it," she says, and gave me the ruler.

Nimbus and me have known each other for a long time. I can't say that being stuck in a trailer too small for him, and with the bottom gone out of it, was the best sort of time to be groping around him and trying to measure things. Jim had to stand in front and hold his ring through the slats and keep giving it a tweak every now and then to take his mind off me because he was trying to get a poke at me all the time.

I told Mrs. Jones that as far as I could see it was about six and a half feet by three and a half. She took this very brightly and said that's just about what she'd reckoned. Would I give her a hand to take off the privvy door? She had a screwdriver and a jemmy ready and said it wouldn't matter a damn to take the privvy door off because it belonged to the gov'nor anyway, and it wasn't as if it faced the road.

We took it off like she said. The latch came off, too, and I handed it to Mrs. Jones. She might want it for another door. It wasn't quite the fit it ought to have been but it was near enough.

There was a good bit of fuss to get it into the trailer under Nimbus's feet. If you've ever tried to slide a privvy door under a bull you'll know what I mean. By the time we moved off again he'd got to the growling stage and when a Jersey starts to growl he's looking for trouble. I unloaded him at Newbank with a mask and two side-lines to be sure.

He's been at Newbank six months now and we shall soon be seeing some calves out of the Island heifers. They should be a bonny lot, with that black face of his. The gov'nor has made no mention of when he'll be brought back to Gale End. Maybe he's thinking the same as me. Maybe Nimbus will end his days there.

If ever we come to sell that trailer, whoever buys it will never be able to make out why the floor has got a neat little window in it!

F.W. White (1965)

Walling Ways

We spend a quarter of the year, off and on, maintaining the dry-stone walls which pattern the fells. Rainscar has about twenty miles of them. Any fine day, no matter what time of year, there is always a gap to be repaired.

Years ago there were many full-time wallers. A good man would complete a rood – seven yards in Yorkshire! – in a day. But that pool of labour has gone. Farmers must do their own walling, and because of labour costs and the time factor there is little new building. Repairing the existing boundaries is a big enough job.

That is why you see much use being made of posts and wire, and wire is also used along the tops of walls which have sunk because they were built on boggy ground. I know of many a good wall that is now no higher than a modern fireplace, and some means must be devised to stop the sheep from leaping over.

The weather is the main enemy of dry-stone walls. Snow lies heavily against them, and when there is a thaw after hard frost sections come shuttering down. I should perhaps add that visitors can co-operate by using the gates!

J.W. Coutes (1957)

A Way of Life

Although farming has to pay, and the better it pays the better we shall like it, we do not judge farming solely on that financial return. It has become the fashion to decry the "Farming is a way of life" idea. Nevertheless a way of life farming is in the sense that another business or profession never can be. If you like the open air, the sun and the wind and the rain, the placid friendliness of cows, the smell of the fields and the farmyard, the happy zest of muscular strength and physical fitness; bacon and eggs for your breakfast, cream on your porridge, and the sight of your children growing up fit and healthy in the country, then you do not mind the long hours, the hard physical work, and lack of freedom – or, rather, of "spare-time".

To be cocking hay or stooking corn on a lovely June or September day when otherwise one might have been noting files in a Whitehall office or teaching a much-too-large class of children; to walk out with the gun and a bundle of snares; to join in the strenuous social activity of a threshing day; to walk down the yard on a winter's night for a last look at cows contentedly munching the sweet-scented hay of summer – all these things bring another reward than the financial one.

Some people believe that the future of farming in Britain lies with large farms and scientific administrators. I believe it lies rather with the small family farm, which is not so susceptible to the winds of economic change. And I believe there are two

types of people who might make the small family farm succeed. The trained ambitious farm labourer starting small and working his way up, still clinging to country traditions and ignoring the attractions of the town; and the man who has started in some business or profession, or in the Services, who has acquired some capital, and who finds the call of farming irresistible.

But the latter must not enter farming with any illusions. It is hard manual work which his family – and any visiting friends – must share. To be safe he must have enough to live on for the first two years. And for that time he will have little leisure and no time to read anything but farming literature. Unless unusually fit he would do well to be under forty when he starts, and whether he has been a rowing man, a footballer, or a professional weight-lifter it will take a full year for his muscles to get adapted to the many peculiar strains and stresses of farm work.

He may never be able to carry a 2 cwt. sack of wheat into the granary from the "corn-end", but when he can fork sheaves on to the thresher for an eight-hour day, then fodder and milk his eight cows without undue fatigue, he will lean over the garden gate to watch the moon rising over the moor and will feel an immeasurable sense of well-being.

William Cowley (1948)

The Daily Round

From Tupping to Tupping

Clapdale is a sheep farm. Over these four hundred acres of land, that stretch from 900-1,100ft. up the side of Ingleborough, sheep have pastured for hundreds of years. However farming may change, as it must to keep in step with a changing world, sheep still will be the main economy of farming here.

Nibbling away at the close limestone turf year after year, daughters following at their mother's heels to learn every inch of the ground they are "heathed" to, these sheep belong here by right of thousands of generations. Certainly we clip them, dip them, and put our mark on them, improve them by introducing fresh tups to them in the autumn and lamb them in the spring, but for all that we are only intruders on their natural way of life. Nothing will ever replace them.

Our farming year starts in October with the annual tup sales. On the choice of a tup depends the stamp of our sheep for many years to come.

In November, the ewes (mainly Swaledale x Dalesbred) are brought inland from the fell. We have rights on Ingleborough, and 130 gaits on other land besides the inland. Then the coupling links are taken off the tups, and they are loosed with the ewes in a hundred-acre field, except for the shearling ewes which are held back for seven to ten days.

They have to be gathered every day for a month, the usual time it takes for all the ewes to have been tupped. So all the dogs get plenty of work and schooling. This farm would be no use without a few good dogs. Half of the time they are working out of sight of the sheep, as the ground is so rough, and a dog that couldn't answer to the hand whistles would be no use at all. We generally have one or two experienced dogs, and one or two young ones being broken in. My husband trains and sells a lot of dogs.

During the first ten days the tups are unmarked. For the next ten days they are keeled, or marked underneath, with red raddle, and for the next ten days with blue raddle. In this way the ewes become coloured on their rumps, and in the spring can be sorted out according to when they are due to lamb.

With the end of tupping time, Christmas is nearly on us, with its short days that make it such a struggle to fit a day's work into a day's light. At the moment we have a diesel engine for our lighting. Perhaps by next winter we shall have the promised mains electricity. When we came here there was nothing but oil, and anyone who has been without electricity will know what a black pit winter can seem. Especially on a wet night. Slip-slopping across a black yard to feed the calves, no proper way to see what you are doing when you get there, fumbling with a flashlight to get the provender, all at a crawl because you can't see properly and – oh, well, it is grand to switch on.

For the next few months we have to hope that it doesn't come too much snow, and especially that it doesn't come without warning. When we have an idea that it will snow the sheep can be gathered inland. Then they can be quickly gathered into a thirty-acre wood where they can't be overblown.

We have some useful sowpy land, with tufts of longish, coarse grass, where the snow soon breaks up to give a bite for the sheep, and we keep some baled hay in a cabin in the woods, as it can be sometimes nearly impossible to sledge it up to the top in deep snow.

Last winter we didn't need to feed any at all. We kept our hoggs at home, instead of sending them away to lower land as is usual. We did mean to give them silage, but the winter was so mild that they did very well with nothing extra at all.

Lambing time starts with us about the second week of April. This year the sheep were very fit after the mild winter, and all had plenty of milk and plenty of mother instinct. After the winter of 1954-5, when the sheep were in poor condition, many of them did not want their lambs, and we spent a weary lambing time trying to mother on odd lambs.

This year we finished with one lamb for every sheep, and a few over, a good average for this type of farm. We don't generally have many twins, and our ewes are better off rearing one lamb well, than twins indifferently. This is the time of year when a sheep farmer wears out his boots, to say nothing of his feet, going endlessly round the fields, checking and re-checking that all is well.

When the lambs are two to three weeks old they are sorted out, injected against pulpy kidney disease, have their ears punched, and our red stripe marked on their sides, then they are turned with their mothers into the pasture instead of the meadow. Later the gimmer lambs and their mothers go to Ingleborough Fell to learn the heath while the wethers and mothers stay inland for better going. The ewes with twins have the best pasture.

The time spent on sorting sheep is considerable, and when someone doesn't close a gate the sorting has to be done again, as the sheep never miss an opportunity to get into a better field. In August, after the lambs are spained, or weaned, all the ewes go to the fell and stay out until tupping time.

The summer days are as long as the winter ones are short. Clipping, dipping, dosing and castrating have to be fitted in among making hay and leading silage. Like most farmers we just keep on so long as the light lasts. We hope sometime to build a better dipper, with proper pens and races to take much of the labour out of handling the sheep. We have miles of dry stone walling, and it is one long battle to keep them in order. They cost nothing in materials, and make better shelter than a fence, but every spare hour can be taken up in walling gaps.

The days seem to fly past. In no time at all the year has almost come full circle, and we are reading the draft ewe and wether lamb sale advertisments in the papers.

Sheila Hammill (1957)

Ploughing out

For the Dales farmer this is the busy season of the year, and because of the exigencies of the time busier than usual. Lambing time is normally a part of the farming cycle that leaves few spare hours and to this has been added the ploughing up and preparation of land for crops.

Bare brown fields scattered here and there among meadows and pasture land already foretell a coming change in our Dales landscape. Corn and root crops will in their season give a new colouring to many a familiar scene and to haytime there will this year be added harvest.

It is not easy to turn over from a traditional form of farming, the sheep and cattle raising for which the Dales country is suited, to a new and unfamiliar form in the raising of crops. A multitude of new problems face the farmer as they would an industrialist who had to convert his factory and plant to a new and unfamiliar product. Whether the outcome of the change will be satisfactory in this part of the country is still uncertain. The Dales farmer is usually neither an optimist nor a pessimist. His attitude is "wait and see". But this year he may be pardoned if he does his waiting a little anxiously.

(1940)

Martinmas Memories

Martinmas may now have little significance, even to those working on the land, but Mart'mas was once a very important time. All farm workers, or farm labourers as they were then called, and many servant girls, renewed their annual contracts with their employers or offered their services to new masters or mistresses. Before doing so, they had a week's holiday and went to their own homes.

In the Holderness area of Yorkshire, to the north, east and west of Hull, the Sunday of the week was a great day. Mothers of the lads and lasses in service were at home. Not all of the offspring had had good places for food during the previous 12 months, so the mothers prepared a great meal, and often a goose was on the menu.

So great were these feasts, we read, that the day became known as "Rahv-kite Sunday". In those parts, *rahv* still means "tear" and *kite* is a word meaning "the stomach". On this Sunday country people ate so much they nearly tore their stomachs apart!

After a week's holiday, the girls and men would go to some agricultural centre like Beverley or York if they wanted a new place. They stood about waiting to be hired. At one time a man or girl could be hired for a long period verbally. About a century ago it was made illegal for hire by word of mouth for more than one year – hence the annual nature of the hirings.

Men would stand in The Pavement or at the end of Parliament Street in the City of York, awaiting the approach of a farmer seeking a labourer. The Martinmas Hirings were a definite part of rural life and though details of the actual engagement varied from place to place, the essentials were the same.

After preliminary questioning as to character, qualifications, ability and perhaps to why the man had left his last place, the farmer would make an offer something like this (an authentic offer made about 45 years ago): "I'll give you £25 a year and a pound extra next Mart'mas if you're a good lad."

The offer would be considered and, no doubt, the prospective servant would at the same time be doing a bit of assessing of his prospective employer.

If, eventually, the farm worker accepted the terms which, of course, included board and lodgings, the deal might well be clinched by the passing of a pound or half-sovereign from the master to the man. The latter was then "bound" for the ensuing 12 months.

In the olden days the servants received what was called a "God's penny" or a "fest" penny to bind them to their bargain, to make the deal "fast". Later, this penny was increased to a shilling and eventually to ten shillings or a pound.

In these days of so-called "folk" music and verse, it is interesting to recall lines that were current in the Pocklington area 100 years ago. They were half-sung and half-spoken in what was almost monotone:

Last Thusk (Thirsk) Hirings as Ah steed brant
Owd greedy comes to me
"Dost tha want hiring, me lad?"
He hired me for a five-pund bill
And Ah was as fast as a thief in a mill,
With a fol de rolyio
Fol de rollydee.

The sum of £25 or £30 does not seem great today, but then it meant a year's savings. Interim payment may well have been made during the year but the bulk of the wages was paid at the end of the term. Comparable riches were available at Martinmas. This was the time when clothiers and footwear dealers made sure that they had good stocks of strong suits and boots ready for the demand that would certainly be intensified.

The prudent and ambitious workers would bank their money, perhaps with a view, eventually, to setting up farming on their own account. There were many who succeeded in doing so, for then the capital requirements bore no relation to those of today.

G.H. Fox (1974)

My Year with Brother Ox

When I was a callow, suburban youth of seventeen I was told I must follow a calling in the Great Outdoors. I listened, though without enthusiasm, and I heard no such call.

In those days, thirty-five years ago, rural postmen were notoriously under-paid, and as for commercial travellers – well, you know the stories told by commercials, and I had been brought up "respectable".

There seemed to be nothing for it but farming, and by sacrificing me to the Goddess of Agriculture the family would be at least assured to an unfailing ability to gratify its taste for home-cured York ham and bacon, to say nothing of milk and honey.

I became a pupil, one of three, on a farm between York and Selby, for a fee which must have made me the most profitable crop on the farm, on an acreage basis.

The potato fields drew first blood. Lifting was in full swing when I arrived, and production immediately slowed down. The horse-drawn "spinner" was followed by a team of casual workers, mostly village girls, who filled stout wicker baskets as they "scratted" the potatoes by hand from the loosened soil. One cart served several furrows and my first agricultural duty was to collect the rapidly filling baskets, carry them to the cart, tip them in, and keep the scratters supplied with empties.

Simple enough? To a flabby, hollow-chested youth, unaccustomed to lifting anything heavier than a succession of spoonfuls of blancmange to his lips, and shod in cast iron boots, leaden with a myriad studs, existence soon became intolerable, and few brief minutes with "drinkings" of stewed tea and heavy pastry offered no respite from the torment.

Stumbling drunkenly up and down soft ridges and hard furrows; tottering unsteady as an octogenarian, twixt cart and scratters; bending down for heavy laden baskets, straining up with feebly wobbling muscles as the baskets neared the almost inaccessible heights of the cart; seeking in vain for unblistered areas of my hands to take the weight of the baskets; life soon became a single unworthy thought – roll on bedtime.

The day's work began at what seemed an indecent hour for washing one's face in cold water and then stumbling sleepily across cobblestones to the covered yard in which bullocks were fattening; the animals – far from receiving the crumbs from the master's table – are in at the first sitting down. Not till they had had their fill could we go into breakfast.

Turnips had to be sliced for them by hand-operated cutter, and carried across the deep straw bedding in bushel measures to the stout wooden tumbrils from which Brother Ox fed. Brother Ox had other notions and did not always wait patiently for his breakfast to reach his plate. Ten tons of assorted hungry beasts, caring nothing for table manners, rarely permitted the first bushel to reach its rightful destination without upturning it into the straw. Indeed, by the pale glimmer of a storm lantern, it was not easy to see the feeding troughs, and one had to walk by faith amongst the unpredictable bumps and hollows.

The small amount of milking was usually done by "Old Bullocky", who was partly deaf and dumb, and whose joy was his pigs. From him I received pantominic instructions in the art of milking, old style, with particular emphasis on the importance of a plentiful application of spit to the hands to facilitate milking.

He found me a discouraging pupil and shortly afterwards he left us, whether in despair or to avoid doing me a mischief, I never discovered. The official explanation was concerned more with his intentions towards the kitchen maid.

Routine jobs for the lesser mortals in winter were thrashing, bagging up potatoes, lifting swedes and mangolds. Ploughing was the prerogative of the aristocracy, the foreman and his first and second horseman. In all matters of horsemanship there was as strict a rule of precedence as exists amongst the domestic staff of some great house.

I was once only allowed to follow the plough for an hour, and actually to hold the stilts or handles for half a furrow. That was the extent of my ploughing tuition, and the first horseman must have suffered agonies of shame lest any passer-by should see and wonder at the strange bulge in his otherwise perfect furrows.

No doubt he also feared for his horse, remembering how poor old Tinker, the most aged and decrepit horse that ever drew a half load at half speed, became mutinous, almost vicious, as soon as I took the reins. Clearly he sensed the opportunity to make a last rebellious horsey protest against Man's dominion over animals by kicking up his heels in the face of a mortal feebler than himself.

His last days must have been made happier with the knowledge that no matter how small the paddock, he could always elude capture by me for as long as he wished to enjoy the spectacle of my humiliation.

I was, however, privileged to observe a similar misfortune befall no less a man than the boss himelf. Someone, deputed to move a lot of poultry from one field to the next, had shifted the hut before the hens had gone to roost. When Mr. T. went his rounds to lock up for the night, he found an empty shed on one side of the fence, and on the other side a bewildered, homeless huddle of hens, clustered together on the former site of their home.

The farcical happenings of the next hour remain one of the few joyous memories in my joyless year. There were the fruitless efforts of three of us, myself as usual largely ineffectual, to persuade, cajole, tempt, threaten, shoo or shepherd some two dozen hens across a mere two dozen yards of ground which they were determined *not* to cross at any price; the stealthy approach with sacks; the shrieks and outraged squawks of the frantic hens, stalked by terror at twilight.

Shocking language came from our respected master and churchwarden, dashing up and down the fence in pursuit of one diminutive poulet. I lost count of the number of times we returned to the *status quo ante* – with the hens still in victorious possession of the site of their old dormitory. The final solution was the capture, one by one, of the unwilling matrons in a flurry of feathers and flapping wings. They were conveyed bodily to their new home. Never were eggs so hardly won as on that day.

Halliday Settle (1958)

Straight Talk from a Farmer's Wife

MISTER EDITOR,

I'm a Yorkshire woman and so I'll come straight to the point. What I want to ask you is this. Why all this glamourising of housekeeping in the country? There's not much glamour about when it's been your job, as it's been mine ever since my husband brought me to this farmhouse getting on for thirty years ago and all that is spent on the home is what's left when the beasts have been comfortably housed.

This is Sunday afternoon when, if everything goes smoothly I do get an hour to myself so I'll just set down my day's work for you to see, and for anyone else who cares to read about it.

I write this in winter time when there is least to do in a farmhouse; for instance no sickly lambs to tend, no newly hatched chicks to feed. Also its Sunday when no extra jobs are done. Usually there's washing or ironing, baking and cleaning to get through as well as the rest.

6-30 a.m. Get up and start calling the boys. Like most young folk they like to go off on their cycles to the pictures on a

Saturday night and it's late when they get home and to bed. So, I can tell you, they take some rousing on Sunday mornings.

Downstairs to make a cup of tea for the boys before they go out to help their Father with the milking – they take him a drink in a can. My man's pretty good and he lights the fire and puts the kettle on before he goes to tend the animals, but he doesn't clean the grate, so this and banking up the fire for the cooking is the first job.

Breakfast. Porridge on the fire and bacon on a paraffin stove, all to be ready and piping hot when they come in from the milking. My husband and one son deliver the milk in the town so breakfast's always taken in a hurry, and I serve them, and wait for mine until they've all gone about their jobs.

What a washing up! Not only our breakfast pots, but the milking pans, too, and all hot water to be carried from the boiler by the fire into the back kitchen. Then the boiler's to be filled up again. Five bucketfuls it takes and as the kitchen pump is frozen to-day all to be fetched from the tap in the yard. The boys brought some up when they came for their breakfast and after the boiler's filled I see to it that the buckets go back as a reminder to them the next time they are coming up.

Sunday dinner to prepare and a batch of scones and apple tarts to bake while the oven's hot for "elevenses". I have a similar baking every day except Monday – washing day. By dint of making a little more than we use each day I tide over Monday. It's going up to eleven now so on goes a kettle or a pan of milk ready for the drink and a bite for the men who never fail to turn up at this time.

Beds to make and the house to tidy. I like to give the living room a spruce up on a Sunday and put the best rugs down, but it's no good laying these until afternoon when the tramping in and out is finished, so I just sweep up, shake and roll up the old rugs, tidy the hearth and dust, and then turn to the back kitchen. Here the floor is to do every day and can't be missed on Sunday or I'd have all the farmyard muck trampled into the house; so up come the mats and round goes the mop.

Drat those hens! They're over the garden wall and scratting away at some daffodil bulbs I've set, hoping to brighten the place up a bit. I'll have to cover them with netting as I can't sit here to shoo the hens off all the time – where was I?

Dinner time. My husband and two sons and a hired man all

hungry from hard work out of doors and I can tell you it needs a pretty full board to satisfy them. And again the washing up! Like most farming folk they like a cup of tea to finish with, as well as again, the milk cans.

Three o'clock. A final touch to the living room and the best rugs laid down and all's tidy except myself. A chair by the fireside looks very tempting but no, not until I'm washed. So upstairs with a pail of hot water from the boiler and a pail of cold, for the country apology for a bath. Into my clean undies and my Sunday clothes and my half day has begun. Just an hour before the men come in for their tea. As soon as I sit down that corner where the paper's leaving the wall strikes my eye and I remember noticing this morning that the kitchen walls are beginning to look dirty. That means lime and paste sometime in the near future, but that's not to-day's job so I won't waste my Sunday afternoon thinking about it.

"Farmer's Wife" (1945)

Farm Folk

Golden Days

In those "olden" days of half a century ago, golden happy days for the farmer, everything on the farm seemed to work according to plan. In the ploughing country, one could, subject to slight variations of weather, tell what work would be in hand, say, ten weeks hence. On the grass farms this ordered rota of things was still more marked. And looking back it seemed as though everything behaved itself.

One did hear of outbreaks of sheep scab which caused the whole countryside to proceed with double dipping operations to the neglect of all other work. There were few forms to complete, and even the weather seemed to behave itself, if what we are told really happened. True, it snowed – and how it snowed – but it came when farmers and countryfolk expected it and were prepared for it. There was no prolonged period of damp, rains and mists, making the pastures into mud flats and the fells into hungry bogs. The sun shone in summer and work went on merrily. Man, beast and land prospered in the warm sun and waxed fat and full of promise. The fell farmer did not boast that he prospered; nevertheless he went about his work happy, working hard and enjoying it all the time.

Farmers of those days were not highly educated. Muck scaling and education were poles apart. Some had great difficulty in writing their names, were bitterly opposed to signing any paper, and paid their accounts in hard cash. They carried round bank notes or sovereigns in a pocket inside their waistcoats. It was almost as though they were undressing when an account had to be paid. They were slow of speech, loyal to a bargain, careful with their hard-earned money, and lovers of good living. Their pleasures were of a simple nature, always associated with stock or farming, and only rarely did they journey away from their immediate Dale. It was from out of that Dale that they found their wives; they were baptised, married and buried in the same Dale church or chapel. Older farmers had only received such meagre education as their parents could afford to give them. Some had been lucky enough to be able to go to the village school where a local lady or the vicar had imparted the famous three R's.

These fell farmers were the simply aristocracy of the countryside. They owed allegiance only to their landlord, the squire, and to him they were at all times deferential. No son or daughter of such a fell farmer would think of entering any other occupation or life than that of farming. Children did not receive any wage; they were content to work for the spending money meted out to them, and they knew that when they were old enough to start farming "the old man" would set them up.

Farming was almost a closed book so far as finance was concerned. Wives had not the faintest idea of the amount of money their husbands had made or had deposited in the bank. The lot of the wife was hard – harder than many women would put up with to-day. They were the unpaid servants of the farm, the slaves of the men who had to weather the storms and looked to the women to provide them with the simple comforts they expected after a hard day on the fells. There were no Women's Institutes, and even if there had been, no woman would have thought she could have spared the time for such 'goings on'. Between feeding the poultry and the calves, separating the milk and making butter, helping with sick animals or tending weak lambs, they baked all the food for huge households. There were big families then and the farms carried more workers. It was a hard life, that of a farmer's wife, harder than that of the farmer, with none of the change which outdoor life gives. In the hayfield she had not only to make the meals and carry them out on to the hayfield, but she was expected to help with all the jobs which are found on a hayfield on a steep slope, after which she would probably give a hand with the milking. These women were the daughters of farmers and were trained in their hard duties.

In those former days there was always plenty of labour available for the fell farms, a notable difference from to-day when farmers are clamouring for more help. Perhaps it was that parents then knew their children would be taught a good trade – and be paid for it while they were learning – and would have plenty to eat. There is still plenty to eat on the farms, but now there are not enough workers to eat that substantial fare. Even the offer to let the men have alternate week-ends off is not attracting future farmers to learn this highly skilled operation. The modern young man, despite the ownership of a motor-cycle, does not care to live on the fells. He has "knocked about more" and knows there are easier jobs than farm labouring. True, the modern farm labourer is much better dressed than the "hind" of a generation or so ago, and he knows much more about matters outside the Dales or on the other side of the fell. He is welcomed in the local dramatic societies, Young Farmers' Clubs and the village Institute. Despite all this and the knowledge that he is the equal or superior in knowledge of any other kind of worker, there is a shortage of workers on the farms.

The farmer himself has changed during the years. He is still the same slow speaking, deep-thinking country lover, but he has travelled more, and is no longer content with occasional days off at local shows. He has become interested in national matters, thinks more politically, and has picked up a good working knowledge of the science of breeding, cultivation, grass management and mechanics. He takes a growing interest in local government, and is keen to see for himself, whenever he can, different methods and styles of farming.

If once the young farmer sought his bride from farms in the same Dale, he has travelled further in his search, and girls from the towns have been brought back as wives to live in antiquated farmhouses. Most have made ideal wives and mothers, coupling that love of animals and rural life with the quick-wittedness of townspeople. They have made the farmhouses more comfortable, introduced new methods, bathrooms, and electricity, where these are possible. They have scrapped those huge fireplaces with the eternal blackleading. They enter into the life of the nearby village, organising socials, concerts, and garden parties. Their work has been eased inasmuch as no longer are they expected to spend hours turning a huge churn to make butter, and not as many loaves are baked. They still yearn for more easily-worked farm houses with the comforts they have seen in the towns, but they recognise it will be some years before those comforts reach out to the fells.

Norman Thornber (1948)

Farmer Joy

Anthony Joy lived alone at a small farm in Hebden Gill. When I first met him, he told me that he was the original "Ben" in William Riley's novel *Jerry and Ben*, and he would proudly point to an old concertina hanging on the ceiling which he said was the actual concertina mentioned in the novel. Others discredited his claim, but after he told me I always called him Ben, a name which seemed to fit far better than Anthony.

He was a true lover of the dales, and particularly of his own neighbourhood. Occasionally he would take a trip to Liverpool or Chester, but he could not stay more than a day or two and was always glad to get back.

He was very fond of reading and in the evenings would sit in his old grandfather's chair with a book in one hand and a candle in the other.

He had a very strong objection to "summer time", and never put his clock or watch forward. "What reight have they to muck about with time," he would say. I asked him what he would do if he had to catch a 'bus or train, and he grudgingly admitted that he had to start an hour too soon. Even when "summer time" was advanced two hours, he still refused to conform to it as far as he possibly could, and when it came to an end he would point proudly to his clock and say, "Look at it, it's reight; and it's been reight all t'time."

One could always be sure of a kindly welcome at his house. I remember once in pre-war days calling at his house to see if I could get some eggs for preserving. "Aye," he said, "I wish you'd cummed sooner, though. I selled them this morning and I've nobbut ten left." I said I should he glad to take those, and when I inquired the price, he said, "They are 1s. 9d. a dozen, so that will be (scratching his head), that will be (still scratching), nay dang it all I'll goa out to t'hen hut and see if I can get two more." Returning after a minute or two he smilingly said, "I've gotten 'em, so now we can do it."

Not only had he an inherent love of the dales; he was also passionately fond of his animals. It was not easy to keep his sheep out of the house. I remember once he was bottle-feeding two lambs. He became very much attached to them and called them Barnum and Bailey. They became such favourites that he would never part with them. Some years afterwards I asked him what had become of Barnum and Bailey. "Oh," he said, "they're out on t'ill side. I'll call 'em," and going out in the yard he shouted "Barnum, Barnum, Bailey." In a few seconds they came running to him.

His dog Roy was also a great favourite, and understood everything that Ben said to him. When I talked with Ben on one occasion, Roy persisted in barking, so Ben said to him, "Roy, goa and fetch t'bulls." These were some distance away from the house, but Roy went off at once and fetched them.

Once I took a party of a dozen or so to camp in one of his fields. One night we arranged to have a sing-song, and invited

Ben to join us, but he was too shy to do this. Meeting him next morning, I told him he had missed a treat. I was much surprised when he replied, "Noa I didn't, I sat at back of t'tent and heeard it all, it were grand."

Since his death the Gill has never seemed the same. One misses his kindly welcome and the merry twinkle in his eyes; and somehow the very landscape, of which he formed a part, seems still to be mourning the loss of a dear friend.

Herbert E. Fletcher (1950)

Uncle Arthur

In July, 1919, I was loitering in York cattle market when someone poked me in the back. It was Uncle Arthur.

"What brings you here, me lad?"

I had been five years in the army and was waiting till college re-opened.

"Loungin' aboot doin' nowt is ruination," he growled. "Better gan back wi' me, we're a'most ready for harvest. You're a big lad, gettin' ower fat and some wark'll do you good, be a nice change after solderin'."

"What's the pay like for harvesting?" I asked.

"*Pay?* Who said owt aboot *Pay?* It's a month holiday I'm offering you! Your Aunt'll be pleased to see you again and Grandma too, *and* your cousin Polly."

Now Polly, the same age as me, was a blonde, and pretty too.

"Well, happen a few days wouldn't hurt me," I said. He smiled and patted me on the back.

"That's me lad! Happen a good man's worth nine pund a month, and his keep. I'll ha' to see how you shape."

The old stone house had two large kitchens. The back one, where the work was done, had a wide open fireplace and an outsized oven; the living kitchen was where the meals were served, where parish meetings took place and dances were sometimes held.

Uncle, Aunt, Grandma and Polly dined aloof at their own table, with its white linen cloth. We hired lads sat on forms at the long bare table. Hams and sides of bacon with sundry bunches of thyme and sage and a few bladders of lard hung from the beams.

The foreman, silent and dignified, presided at our table as we cleared our piled-up plates. I marvelled at the men's appetites and capacity – until I had worked with them in the fields. I slept in the men's "chaimber" above the back kitchen, climbing to it by a step-ladder that reached the trap-door. We left our boots in the kitchen.

In this big "chaimber" each lad had his box holding his Sunday clothes and treasured possessions. We hung our working "togs" from pegs on the rafters and slept like logs on our straw mattresses till a loud hammering on the trap-door roused us each morning.

It was Grandma, then turned eighty, sounding reveille with a stout walking stick.

"Five o'clock, men! Time you were up!"

Sometimes I heard her banging on Uncle Arthur's door too. "Gone five already! Do you hear me? If your poor father had been alive he'd ha' gone crazy, you getting up at this time o' day."

I usually fed the squealing pigs – six or seven dozen of 'em – then let the poultry out and helped Polly feed them while the lads in the stable were "doing" their horses. Breakfast at six found me relishing our homely fare, usually huge slices of cold bacon with plenty of fat, and red pickled cabbage.

We "opened out" each corn field, mowing a swathe round the outside. I took my turn with the scythe and a back-breaking job that was too. Then when the binders swept round, each dragged by three great Shire horses, I was kept stooking till dark. We often worked a fourteen hour day.

"More rain, more rest," someone said, but I hated wet days. Then we'd be in the fields setting up fallen sheaves, rebuilding stooks, with sacks tied round our waists and our legs and feet sopping wet. I hated most the bearded barley for its awns clung to me, worked away into my underclothes and down my back. Harvest bugs too itched unbearably – worse than lice at Gallipolli.

One morning, when the rain fell in torrents, Uncle Arthur recited mournfully the Ryedale farmers' lament:

"Rainin' ageean, Ah deea declare.
It's twea days wet for ya day fair."

until he came to these two lines, which he quoted fiercely, looking at me all the time:

"Harvest foaks wages gannin' on,
AN' there tha stand, an' NOWT is done!"

I took the hint and mended some doors and gates, then made him a new 'creel' (a wooden stretcher to carry a slaughtered pig). There was seldom a slack minute, though we had one day holiday, to visit Ryedale Show at Kirkbymoorside. Uncle showed a young horse and Polly entered butter and eggs. She and I cycled over and stayed for the dance in the marquee and got home well after midnight.

Next day Grandma threatened to take her stick to my back for "keeping your poor little cousin out so late." I could hardly be expected to tell her that it was the other way round!

Uncle Arthur took me into the front room at the month end and wrote me a cheque.

"Nine pund, it should ha' been, but I'll make it ten. You've turned out better'n I expected."

Stephen Kirby (1966)

Mary Robinson of Tosside

Mary Robinson went as a tall, auburn-haired young bride to Brockthorne, a 300-acre farm, and cooked, washed and cleaned, bore four sons and eight daughters, all alive today. Never a week passed but chance visitors were invited to a meal and, in addition to the large family, cousins, landlords' sons and shooters' daughters, often spent happy holidays there. What woman today would face undaunted the everlasting washing and ironing, churning and buttermaking, baking, cooking and cleaning in a remote farmhouse, with no modern aids?

When her eldest son was accidentally shot in the eye by a careless shooter seeking rabbits, there was no panic. The horse was harnessed, a little bed prepared in the bottom of the trap, and the six mile journey to the doctor started. Another crisis did not find her wanting. Her second boy, Billy, was climbing up the wheel of a cart, in charge of a farm man, when the horse started. He fell and the wheel grazed his scalp. He was carried home with a great gaping wound oozing blood. While her husband rushed to summon the doctor, she bravely staunched the blood with a mixture of rum and cream, as her mother had once done. The doctor duly arrived, stitched up the wound and soon the little boy was running about again.

Each of her children had allotted tasks about the household. The girls were taught to knit, sew, embroider, peg rugs, make quilts, and be able to lend a hand about the house and kitchen. In the midst of a seventy-acre haytime there would be blackcurrants and raspberries to make into jam in a huge brass pan on an open coal fire that burnt the legs as the sweet jam was stirred.

In haytime, too, there would be two Irishmen to house and feed for four or six weeks, and often six men sat down to the six meals each day. On "dipping" days, the neighbours took their sheep to the modern bath her husband built in the yard and made it a community affair, with as many as fifteen men feeding round the huge kitchen table.

As a special treat, she would light the fire under a "bakestone" in the wash-house and stand for hours baking oatcakes and crumpets. The former were hung to dry on the kitchen clothes rack, near the ceiling, and were often mistaken by townsfolk for so many washleathers.

After retiring from the farm, her husband died and she faced life alone in a small cottage. She had a host of friends to call on her, all of whom she welcomed with a cup of tea. Finally, after only a week in bed, she was carried to her last rest at Tosside by four stalwart sons-in-law, surrounded by more family and friends than the church pews could hold.

Margaret F. Glossop (1950)

Farm Lads

The farm lads of East Yorkshire were such characters, and their lives so vastly different from those employed on farms today. On the larger farms, often around 1,000 acres, the unmarried men "lived in" at the foreman's house. This was good-sized and well-built, standing 100 yards or so from the big farmhouse. Both were protected by the usual "shelter belt" of hardwood trees, without which life would have been a bleak prospect on the high windswept hills.

The foreman's house was known as the "hind's house" and the foreman's wife, the "hind's wife". It was her job to provide beds for the men, two to a double-bed, in a large dormitory-like bedroom, and to feed them at a long scrubbed table in the big kitchen.

The beds were mostly joiner-made, with plain wood head-boards and metal or wooden slats on which a hard mattress was often topped by a feather bed, with coarse sheets, and brown blankets. Furniture and bed linen were supplied by the farmer, but washing was done by the hind's wife and, of course, there was a constant succession of baking days.

The lads, perhaps eight or nine of them, had pies at every meal – yes, even breakfast, after a good helping of cold, boiled bacon (mostly fat) with dry bread, and tea in an enamel mug. In earlier days they were only allowed skimmed milk, as that was always plentiful, and tea was considered a luxury. The milk was served in basins. Bread and jam was a treat for Sunday tea.

Broth, a soup made chiefly from vegetables, was cooked in the old fire-coppers, and also appeared in basins. The main course at the mid-day dinner was always filling. Boiled beef appeared frequently, and large puddings – Yorkshire or suet – were served before the meat. Steamed or boiled suet puddings with treacle made a satisfying sweet and a change from pie – which also appeared at teatime, and was more often than not accompanied by cold fat bacon again! This five o'clock meal had to last the lads till breakfast time. It was considered that good (if tough) pastry lasted in the stomach far better than bread, and made one strong, hence the derisive remarks about the weakness of "narrow-chinned-bread-and-butter townies!"

Under a good foreman, the lads learned to "look sharp" and not to waste time over meals. At one farm near Birdsall, where the foreman's house was some distance from the buildings, it was said that "if you tumbled over a stone on the way to dinner, it wasn't worth going for you'd have missed it!"

On farms not large enough to warrant a foreman's house, the unmarried labourers were fed in the farm kitchen, often the men's kitchen, while the farmer and family ate in the front kitchen.

The men's bedroom was always situated at he top of the back staircase often with the open rail at the top forming the entrance to the room. There were air vents in the ceiling, presumably to give air in days when windows would be rarely opened.

Each lad had a wooden box by his side of the bed, and this contained his clothes and worldly goods, with a secret compartment for valuables. Money was scarce when wages were paid only at Martinmas, and if cash was needed for some particular purchase during the year one had to ask the farmer, or maister, for a sub!

Clothes were made to last. Shirts (collarless) of strong white cotton striped in blue, or black with long "laps" as underpants, were seldom worn; vests with sleeves were used all the year round.

Waistcoats and "fustin" jackets lasted a long time, and corduroy was so thick that breeches or trousers seldom wore out. They had cotton linings too – so perhaps it is as well that in those days of laborious washdays it was not considered necessary to wash these garments often.

The farmer's wife never washed the personal clothes. Some relation took on this chore, so one saw the lads setting off on a Saturday afternoon with their bundle of "weshing". Some were lucky enough to be able to bathe, in a tin bath before a kitchen fire. The only ablutions in the farmhouse were performed in an enamel bowl at the bath kitchen sink, the cold water coming from the pump, and hot from a can filled from the boiler at the side of the big black range in which a fire burned, for cooking and baking, all seasons of the year.

The outside privy, so cold in winter and odorous in summer, was not for the men either. They had to manage as best they could in a corner of the foldyard. This was also the tipping place for the "closet" buckets, tipping being an unpopular task.

The day's work began early. The womenfolk had to rise early, too, in order to get the fire range hot to boil the water for breakfast. With horses to feed, muck out, and harness up, before the long hours of field work, the young lads must have grown very weary before the time came to "lowse out".

Changing seasons brought changes of jobs – ploughing, drilling, harrowing and rolling. They meant a long mileage of walking behind horses. "Plugging muck" was hard, too. I remember my late father-in-law saying: "Well, they'll never get a machine to do this job!" What a relief it must have been when the great foldyards were cleared of the winter's accumulation of well-rotted straw and bullock manure.

Hoeing the root crops was a change, also "luking", a strange term for chopping out thistles from growing corn. Haytime and harvest, with still longer working hours, were relieved by the welcome sight of the "lowance" baskets, and brief rests beside haycocks or stooks in the golden fields.

Threshing days, perhaps the busiest of all, were dreaded by most farm households. The lads enjoyed the extra chat and gossip as men from neighbouring farms came in to help. The work was hard, especially for the "corn-carriers" (eighteen stone sacks to be humped up steep granary steps) and for the four "caff lads" who spent their day in a cloud of dust as they struggled beneath a large "sheet" of caff held by the four corners, and nearly burying the carrier.

In the house all was a frantic rush, with extra baking beforehand, and a "tea" to provide for the two men who arrived the previous night with the traction engine. They were at the farm early the next morning, "getting steam up", and so they were in for their breakfast, too. Then "lowance" to be ready by 9.30 for a dozen or more.

Extra men attended the mid-day dinner (which often featured huge meat-and-tatie pies). "Lowance" came again at three o'clock, and if the stack (or perhaps more than one) wasn't finished the same procedure continued during the next day.

Hours were long, and work was hard, in the old days of farming, but there was a happy comradeship, and a pride in one's work. Only recently, a middle-aged lorry driver called at our farm, and remarked that he'd been hired "first year off" in the district. He recalled: "Those were good days, and we enjoyed life; it's not the same nowadays."

Irene Megginson (1977)

Land Girls

Three Girls

They stood there waiting. Just three girls, the "last of many" I called them. They had stood there many times, and as I passed them once a week I stopped my car and picked them up. I was only too glad to give them a ride, but this time they told me there would not be many more times they would ride with me. Just three girls, but something more than mere girls – for they were three members of the Women's Land Army. Three town girls who had come into the country four years ago and had ploughed, sown and reaped, and housed our valuable food crops. Now they were going to see the last harvest housed and then would leave the country to go back to town life.

They were typical of the many who came to the Craven country, giving up their home life to live in a hostel. Often there were others with them, newcomers who were being taught the intricacies of tractors and the art of ploughing a straight furrow; odd work for girls like Marion, whose father was in the police force at Huddersfield; Little Midge, from Rotherham, a book-binder who became a ploughing champion; and Margaret, the Head Girl and a former private secretary. But these three, Janet, Nancy and Ruby, were the last of the originals who broke down the farmers' antipathy to "them there Land Girls" and showed they could plough and work equal to any men.

They had stood there in all kinds of weather. I had picked them up when they were almost frozen with cold, their hands frost-bitten and their noses blue. There had been times when they were wet through and their overalls caked with mud from the plough fields. Then there were the times when they had been leading lime on to the land and their eyes were red rimmed, or perhaps it was basic slag which coated their face and hair with dark dust. They seemed glad of my lifts and I enjoyed their company. Gradually I got to know them and joked with them and talked with them about the kind of work they were doing and what they had done before they came to the rescue of our crops.

Lest I be thought to favour any of the three, let me deal with them alphabetically. Janet, a dressmaker from near Ilkley, was the one who came in for most teasing. There was always some joke we could enjoy, even though she accused me of "picking on her". Once, when I went to see them in a ploughing competition, Janet turned a baneful eye on me, but I found afterwards the ploughing was not going as well as it ought. No wonder for the field was a sea of mud. Nancy, a clerk from the Castleford district who worked in Leeds, was the quietest of the trio. She had all the blarnet of the "Ould Country", from which she originally hailed, and her ready smile and the colour of her hair gave her away. Ruby was more at home with horses than with horse power. She knew all the points of a horse, for she helped with a Riding School near Mirfield.

Of course there have been others. Dorothy, who married a local farm worker, and Joan, who walked out of the hostel one week-end and returned a married woman. She is still in the W.L.A., but I gather the rest of the clique have not forgiven her for not having let them know of the big event.

N.T. (1947)

Memory Knocks

I opened the door this morning to a beautiful day, and once again, for a brief moment, I wished that I were back.

It is five years now since I brought my tractor for the last time into Skipton depôt – five years of home and housekeeping, of husband and children – happy, fruitful years. But oh, still in my heart – on warm spring mornings such as this, on hay-scented summer evenings, and on sparkling days of winter frost – memory knocks!

How happy we were – forty Yorkshire girls in a Land Army hostel in Skipton, living and working in lovely Craven! Memories surge in upon me, and familiar faces come to mind. Just for a while I'll daydream.

I think I treasure most the friendships. How kindly was the farmer's wife in Addingham, who would never let me stand a moment for the bus, which stopped outside her door. It was:

"Cum in, lass, theer's a cup o' tea for thi and a bite o' summat."

And I went in and sat among fat homely cushions, and gazed at an array of cross-work samplers on the walls and tapestries adorning every chair.

There was "Old Harry", a one-eyed war veteran of 1914-18, also a war-ag. tractor driver. I worked with him for two years and loved to hear his soft Warwickshire drawl. He was full of a disarming conceit, and would never admit a mistake. His one eye would quell and cow any who dared to question his judgment. He had a wife and eleven children who lived in the East Riding, and he never tired of telling me about them, as we sat in the barn sorting 'taties' on wet days.

Then there was "Old Dick" – round and smiling in contrast to Harry's lanky dourness. The two men were bitter rivals; each claimed to be the best ploughman on the job, and each was loud in his denunciation of the other. If Dick worked six hours' over-time one week, Harry would do seven the next; and there was one joyful day when they worked in the same field and almost killed themselves in their effort each to plough the bigger "half".

So many names come to mind – Jock and "Slowitt", "Duckfeet" and "Jungle Bug" – all gone now, as most of the men have gone, to jobs in other counties, for they are plough-men, and the dales are green once more. Of the girls, several remained, and some, like myself, are farmers' wives, living in Skipton, Ilkley and Gargrave – staid matrons now.

How I loved the sight of a turning furrow with the seagulls and wagtails following behind my tractor! How I delighted to ride on the back of a bouncing seed-drill, with a mackerel sky above and a pungent smell of earth and fertilizers and paraffin fumes to assail my nostrils.

What glorious days we spent singling turnips, setting "taties" or leading hay! And oh, the joy of harvest time, to ride the binder and watch the falling grain hit the canvas and travel through, then hear the click as it dropped behind. Another sheaf!

Oh no, Joan, Nora, Edith, May, Ann and all of you – land girls with me – I haven't forgotten the backaches and blisters, the late nights and soakings, nor the disdain of the factory girls when, dirty and dishevelled, we sat beside them in the bus. No, I haven't forgotten, but to-day, in the spring sunshine, with a jug of daffies and catkins on the table, and Rumbold's Moor, golden-green and dotted with lambs, beckoning through my window – sentiment is my master. I feel the prick of tears in my eyes, and once again, for just a little while, I wish I were back!

Hazel Chew (1949)

Ploughing the Fields

On that first morning George took me to plough at a farm way off the road, down a rough, precipitous track with a frightening drop at one side and a camber that seemed determined to tilt us off into the abyss below.

For once, my memory forsakes me. I can remember nothing more than that, probably because I was petrified with fright as I looked down the road I was to follow and watched George's retreating back as he jogged ahead of me.

I stayed at the top and waited for him to notice. The noise of

his own tractor drowned the sound of mine and he carried on, oblivious to the mutiny behind him. The track snaked, like the Burma Road, down the hillside and, eventually, out of his eye corner, as he retracked across below me, he saw me and looked up.

I was near to tears because it looked like certain death to me, even more so as I'd seen George wobbling and rocking his way down. I shook my head vigorously, wondering what on earth had prompted me to come into the Land Army.

George dismounted and slowed his engine down a tick-over. He tightened the length of the binder twine that held his coat together and came back with purposeful tread. He stepped up behind me, his hand on the mudguard. "What's ter do?" he demanded. "Lost thi nerve as 'ta?"

"I daren't go down there," I croaked. "Isn't there another way?"

George shook his head: "Cum on," he said, "tha's all reight – shove 'er into bottom – get thi foot off t'clutch, low gear's thi best brake – *get thi foot off!*"

Slowly we moved forward and downward. I resisted the temptation to use the brake, which was rather doubtfully combined with the clutch. George hung on behind me: "That's it – pull 'er ovver a bit; not so fast, gentle now – keep 'er at that."

Snail-like we joggled down the hillside until we came to a stop behind George's own tractor, halfway to the bottom. "Tha'll manage now," he said, "just follow me – I'll go slow."

Sweat stood on my brow, my hands were clammy, my stomach contracted but I made it: triumphantly we came into the farmyard at the bottom of the hill.

"Which field maister?" George asked the farmer who was pig-feeding along the yard. The man looked up, taking in the sight of a second tractor with ill-concealed apprehension.

"Mornin' George – 10 acre – across t'beck."

We chugged on. In my relief I was near delirious and broke into song, but my joy was short-lived, Along the little leafy lane we turned a corner and came upon a beck with a two-foot drop into it and another one out on the other side.

They didn't – they couldn't – expect us to drive across that. *They* did – and *we* did. A nose dive, then a perilous tilt at the other side and we were there, in the field.

"Tha nivver needs to worry about goin' straight up an' down,"

George said earnestly. "It's driving on a slant tha's got to watch – that's when tha could roll to t'bottom i' quicksticks. Remember that – allus tak it straight up and down then tha can't go wrong." It was sound advice and I always heeded it.

Ploughing was enjoyable. Best of all was breaking into virgin grassland and seeing it roll so straight and even, not crumbling like the jagged edges of last year's stubble crop.

The Craven farmers did not see it that way, and who could blame them? It was a district ill-suited to the plough, so hilly that many fields could only be ploughed one-way, that's to say that the ploughman carried his plough idle to the top of the hill and only lowered it on the downward run.

Worst of all it was the pirating of grazing land that was so precious to the hill farmer, of the meadow that had given him valuable hay over countless generations. But the War Agricultural Committees decreed and the farmers grumbled, swore and obeyed.

So there we were, in our first field, and George gave me a brief outline of how the plough worked and what my part in the proceedings would be. I watched him pace out the field into even sections, marking it with twigs; then, to cut his first straight furrow across the field, he put a stone on the farther wall and a tall wand of birch halfway across.

"Tha sees that," he said. "That's me straight line – when I can see that stick i'line wi' yond stone, and keep it that way reight across t'field, I'll not get far out."

I watched the first black scrape, just a single furrow, only shallow at the first cut then the re-track over the same ground, turning it back, deeper this time and toppling two more on top of it.

His first mark had been true, and the furrows ran straight as a die. "Come on," George shouted, "follow me in next time round – drop thi plough just afore tha comes in – that's reight – we're off."

It seemed so easy that I couldn't go wrong. I must keep the tractor wheel nudging the edge of the last cut, watch for stones and lift the shares to ride over them. Any waverings I made were corrected by George the next time across.

I found myself lulled into a false sense of security. Then, driving towards a huge beech tree, so near the end of my row that I was already leaning down to lift the plough there was a sickening jerk. I almost took a header over the back. The tractor reared slightly on its back wheels and the engine stalled. At the same time there was an ominous bang behind me.

George was halfway along the field. It seemed ages before he got back to my end. "Now what?" he demanded, with an air of suffering.

"I've hit something," I told him needlessly, and we surveyed the tangle of splintered wood, the smashed ploughshare, the churned-up ground.

"Roots," he said disgustedly. "Tha should a' been ready for 'em, lifted her a bit sooner. Still tha weren't to know lass, I should a' warned thee." He boarded my tractor, eased it gently back until the plough tilted and released itself from the labyrinth of beech roots that had held it fast.

Then he fetched spanners from his toolbox and replaced the broken share. "Tha'll be wary next time," he said. "Trees that size 'ev roots a bloody mile." He said it mildly, almost gently. He was not given much to swearing.

Hazel Driver (1974)

From a Land Girl's Log

An adventure with a cow today!

We walked from Hellifield through Otterburn and along the Airton road to the barn where we had left the tractor. As we were filling it with not-too-clean water, using the leakiest bucket in the world, a farmer's man rushed round the corner shouting for help. Off we dashed to find a cow in a pit of liquid manure. The poor creature was out of its depth and in a sorry plight indeed. Fortunately our foreman was with us and between us we managed to hold the cow's head up, one girl clinging to its tail. Another ran to tell the farmer and get a rope. He hobbled up with his two sticks and shouted orders and cursed while we tied the rope round the cow's neck and hind quarters. We heaved and tugged but hadn't sufficient strength between us and had to hold on to the rope until two farmers in their best breeches came tramping down the road, probably on their way to the auction. They quickly came to our aid and together we pulled until the poor frightened creature came out, with such an odour that we nearly passed out on the spot. However, it stood on its four legs and later was reported to be chewing the cud, apparently none the worse for its dip.

Mary Sykes (1944)

Letter to a Land Girl

Dear Louie,

Do you remember when you first came to our farm? It was harvest time 1942.

"I'm the new land girl," you said shyly.

"Oh hell!" said the Boss. He surveyed you gloomily. It must have seemed an unkind greeting – but you were the third new land girl in three days. The first had cycled the three miles from the Hostel, and had been shown by our horseman, John, how to set up the sheaves of corn correctly, to defy wind and rain. Cycling back at the end of the day she had got soaked in a sudden rainstorm.

The next morning another girl arrived. "June's gone sick. I'm Maureen," she announced briskly. John, a patient man, demonstrated the art of "stooking" once more. She told us at lunchtime that she'd been a cinema usherette before the war. She'd seen 'Scott of the Antarctic' 48 times. After working hard all day, she cycled off with a cheery "see you tomorrow". But it was you who had to explain that Maureen had tried horse-riding the night before, and had fallen off, and hurt her leg.

You were quieter than the other girls, but that harvest-time we got to know and like you. You told us that your parents were dead, and you lived with an older sister and brother. Since

leaving school you'd worked in a carpet factory – harder work than farming was your eventual verdict.

I remember how willingly you tackled the unfamiliar farm jobs in all weathers. Harvest was followed by potato-picking, and sugar beet lifting; back-breaking work in those unmechanised times.

It must have been a dreary bike ride back that winter, along cold country lanes, with not a glimmer of light in the blackout. But I never heard you grumble.

Early in 1943 we asked you to come and live with us, and you said you would. A woman recruiting officer came to arrange the transfer. She said that if she'd known we wanted someone to live-in, she could have got us a girl she'd interviewed recently, from a very good home – "lilypond and all that," she added. I assured her that you were the one we wanted. We never saw her again, but the phrase she'd coined was a quote in our family long after its origin was forgotten.

You lived with us for four years. Every Saturday after lunch you set off to cycle the familiar three miles to catch a bus to the big city, and then another to your native town.

You said that you only went home for the fish and chips. But I knew that you missed your brother, and the sister who had looked after you for years. Without fail you came back at ten-thirty every Sunday night, wobbling up the cart-rutted drive on your bike.

Our five-year-old daughter was very pleased you'd come to live with us, but didn't know how it was possible that you didn't know about wild flowers. Thanks to her dad, she could name the scores of flowers that grew in the little wood, and on the headlands. When you walked in saying "Look! the first buttercup," she said kindly, "Well, it's really called a celandine, Louie."

That year the war news was sombre, and everyone had worries and secret fears. News from your domestic front came as a light relief. "Our Evelyn managed to get a tin of paint cheap – so she went mad and painted everything in sight."

"That'll clear things up a bit," I said.

"Yes – it's aluminium paint."

Do you remember the time you took two rabbits, shot in the harvest field, home to your sister to help out the meagre meat ration? She laboriously plucked one, and then, fed up and smothered in fluff, told you to take the other to the man at the fish shop, and ask him to pluck it. You said he nearly died laughing.

One Sunday night you came back and said you'd fallen out with them, and weren't going home the next weekend.

But, knowing that your brother was due to be called up any time, I persuaded you to go. "They'll have to apologise though," you said. You came back smiling. You'd found them both sitting behind the big clothes-horse, on which was hung a notice – "Keep Out. Dangerous Animals", and you'd had to laugh.

Only once did you sulk in our house, and that was the fault of Boss. It was the end of yet another harvest, and thinking you looked tired out, he told you that he and the two men could get the last load from the far field without your help. You came in from the stockyard, silent, miserable and jiggered. You were too shy to tell him how much you had wanted to ride proudly back on top of that last swaying wagon-load. After all, you had been part of the team for weeks.

Talking of swaying loads, do you remember the day you shot off the top of a cart-load of hay, as John led the horse round into the fold-yard? You landed on your back in a mass of deep organic muck! But no bones were broken, it was a soft landing. Winter though it was, I made you strip off before you came into the house!

Lady Bingley was the Women's Land Army Liaison Officer, who visited our farm at intervals to see if you were happy. She always had a private talk with you. We both liked her. One day it was pouring with rain, and I told her you were helping me in the house. "That's all right, if Louie doesn't mind. Lord Bingley has to help these days; he peels potatoes, and cleans boots and shoes." I pointed out to Boss one of the advantages of not being a lord.

Just once I saw Lady Bingley again. Now quite old, she was sitting placidly knitting as we, the public, passed through her stately home. I mentioned the name of our farm, and asked if she remembered coming to see the land girl who lived with us – 25 years ago.

"Yes, indeed I do. Louie. A very nice little gel," she said firmly.

It is 1991 now, and I am quite old.

Goodbye, Louie, and "Thanks for the memory".

Jean B. (1991)

Farmers and sheep gather at Muker Show, Swaledale *(J.C. Moore)*

Temple Newsam Home Farm, near Leeds *(Clifford Robinson)*

Geese at Gayle, Wensleydale *(J.C. Moore)*

Sheep-clipping besides the Buttertubs Pass *(Clifford Robinson)*

Model farm equipment at Hasholme Carr Farm (*Jack Snowden*)

Gap-walling at Malham *(Eric Bland)*

Harvesters at Holme on Spalding Moor *(Frank Dennison)*

The cattle section at Kilnsey Show, Upper Wharfedale *(Clifford Robinson)*

Sheep Talk

The "Golden Hoof"

One associates fell farming with sheep, "the golden hoof", for sheep provided the chief income of the highland farmer. The owner of the flock drew money from the sale of the wool, the lambs and the draught ewes. A newcomer on the fells bought, of necessity, most of the flock of the man who was leaving his holding, for these sheep were "heathed"; they had been bred on the farm, knew where the "bield" or shelter was, and could safely be left to fend for themselves when there was a rush of other work on the farm.

The hardy Scotch sheep were the more popular, although some farmers kept a few halfbred sheep from which they bred lambs for the butcher. The trouble was that these sheep had to be brought off the fells in winter. Often they were sent to lower land, preferably to the arable country, where they were folded on turnips. The fell farmer paid so much a head for this keep, while the farmer on whose land they were folded had the benefit of the dung with which they fertilised his land.

It was hard work to be able to farm without obtaining long credits from the feeding-stuff merchants and other traders who supplied goods for the farm. Such merchants always knew that they would be paid ultimately, but not until the sheepmen had drawn their money for the wool, lambs, and redundant sheep.

Good shepherds were born, not made, and they had to serve a long apprenticeship before they were admitted to be able to "ken" sheep. That was the day of sheep salving, when, instead of immersing the animals in a bath of warm greasy fluid, each sheep was turned over and a mixture of Stockholm tar, lard and whale oil was taken on the ends of the fingers and rubbed into the opened fleece. This was done each autumn, and in the summer the sheep were passed through some dammed up stream for their summer dipping.

Shepherding on the moors was done either by a whole-time shepherd, paid in proportion to the number of rights each farmer had or, on the smaller moors, was done by some young farmer just starting up. In lambing time special men were brought in to tend the ewes in their birth pangs. The lambing man had some small bothy or corner of a building and for a month or so had complete charge of the entire flock. These men had their own old-fashioned remedies, some of which are still used, but many have been ousted by modern scientific knowledge. They were the kings in their little world and perhaps for a month would never have their clothes off for a sleep. I have heard a farmer say that one year's good lamb crop in those days paid two years' rent of the fell farm.

Norman Thornber (1947)

Shepherd Thomas Joy

Thomas Joy, now 75, has kept himself robustly busy since he left school at the age of 13 "and a month or two". He was born at Moorside, Hartlington. His father, who had the grand-sounding name of Horatio Bowden Joy, was a quarry-man, farm labourer and then a farmer on his own account. Thomas went first to Hebden School, then to Grassington, and he was not formally released from the stress of education.

He recalls, with a chuckle, that one morning his brother, in urgent need of the horse to perform an errand, could not get into the stable. The horse, gravely ill, was lying behind the door. By the time the family had sorted out the problem, Thomas – who had been left in bed – was far too late for his lessons. He was not roused on successive days. In due course, the head-master inquired whether or not he intended to return to school. "I didn't say anything; I never went back!"

His home from 1920 to 1936 was Gill House, some three miles from Grassington. This family, like many another, experienced the cruel years of the Slump, which was at its worst in the early 1930s. "We sold some good horned lambs about 1932 for 6s. 6d. each; we just couldn't keep 'em." Father kept to the same strain of Shorthorn cattle from 1910 "until the finish." There were both red and roan cattle. Mother used some of the milk for making butter and cheese.

Grassington Moor has for long been a sheep-run. Men at 13 local farms formed the Grassington Sheep-Keepers' Association, and they met on the last Monday in March to hire a shepherd. Two bye-law men saw that the farmers kept to the rules of the Moor; "they got to be four!"

The job of shepherd was advertised in the *Craven Herald*. In 1940, four people were interested, and put in tenders for the work. It was unwise to pitch the price too high, and Thomas decided on 38s a week. He began shepherding on Grassington Moor on April 1. (In 1946, his income rose to £3.5s a week. The farmers' secretary was paid £5 a year, but "he'd not a big lot to do.")

A Dales shepherd worked more by the calender than a watch; there were regular annual jobs, but the weather ruled. Pennine weather is rarely helpful, offering a chilly spring, cloudy summer, and a long winter, with snow or jangling ice.

In hard weather, Thomas Joy reached the edge of the moor to find up to 700 sheep congregating on this low ground. He would drive them higher, but "they stayed about an hour and then crept back again." It was vital that the Moor should be evenly grazed, and there should be no great concentration of animals in one spot.

In spring, the lambing sheep were taken from the Moor. Any late-lambers were not distrubed for another fortnight or so. The ewes, with their new lambs, returned in the middle of May. Then, just before shearing, came the washing of the sheep. The beck was "demmed" with stones and sods to create a sizeable pool.

About 1,000 sheep were gathered and brought down to the nearby fold, from which each animal was manhandled to the pool. Two men took one sheep, one man grabbing the breast, the other the buttocks, and they deftly turned the animal upside down before tossing it into the water, from which it swam as best it could. True washing, or "dollying", was in an earlier period, and at that time a serious attempt was made to wash the underparts of each sheep.

Ten days after washing, the shearing commenced. There was another "gather", and the separation of the immense flock into the groups belonging to each of the farmers. In summer, Thomas Joy was much aware of insect pests, especially flies, for in humid weather there might be an infestation of maggots which, if not attended to, would lead to the deaths of many of the sheep.

A maggot-ridden sheep was a sorry sight. From it came a distinctive smell. Mr. Joy had a dog, the speciality of which was detecting such sheep by scent. "We used to rub fine, dry peat on a sheep's skin if it was not broken; it was said to discourage the flies from striking... I've seen sheep covered from shoulders to tail with maggots... The problem has been alleviated by modern dips."

In summer, too, he was watchful for rigged sheep, or for the hogg that might have caught a horn in its wool and was walking wearily round and round. A sheep which at shearing time had not been adequately cleaned out between the legs, and its tail was not adequately clipped, might pick up pieces of heather, with the result that it walked awkwardly and painfully. There was no day on the Moor without its special task.

Another "gather" was for spaining, the separation of ewes from their now lusty lambs. The last "gather", at the end of October, was so that the ewes could be put to the rams. They stayed in the pastures until the beginning of December, when once again they were driven back to the Moor.

Thomas Joy knew his Moor so well he was never lost. He advises anyone who has missed his way in poor conditions to seek out a stream and follow it down, or to note – before the onset of mist – on which cheek the wind is blowing, and keep that cheek cooled by the wind.

He has seen many strange sights, none more curious than the sheep and lamb he found, side by side, and quite dead. They had been struck, simultaneously, by lightning!

(Thomas Joy died in March 1982)

W.R.M. (1982)

Straying from the Fold

Farming on the Wolds means mostly corn – and sheep. When we congregate the talk is invariably of ewes and lambs, gimmers, tegs, hogs, shearlings and whethers; when we debate it is often to compare Leicesters, Border Leicesters and Suffolks.

Last winter we talked for some weeks about certain sheep that had strayed from the fold. My farmer friend, Amos Hoggard, took a casual look at his flock in the turnip field one morning, then counted them. He rubbed his eyes and counted again. There were eighty too many! Mind you, we do get a few wanderers occasionally, but eighty was almost another flock! He rang up all his neighbours and local shepherds, checked and re-checked, but nobody had lost even one ewe lamb. Finally, after a day or two, he notified the police and they sought everywhere for the owner.

One week passed – ten days – a fortnight, but still the eighty remained, eating Amos Hoggard's turnips. Three weeks went by, and the whole countryside was agog; at long last, at a farm a few miles away, a flock was found to be eighty short! In our local inn, where the shepherds meet, it was the sensation of a lifetime. "Sike a thing 'ad nivver 'appened 'ere in t'memory o' man!"

Stephen Kirkby (1958)

Waltzing Matilda

On a still autumn day, when the sunlight cut cleanly through the sky, unhindered by cloud, I made the acquaintance of Matilda, one of the moorland sheep which are the unpaid but persistent green-keepers of Goathland.

These hill sheep – Scotch black-faced and Swaledale crosses – have a robust disposition which enables them to match up to the rigours of the moors. There is a remarkable heaf system under which certain flocks instinctively keep to a particular tract of land.

At Goathland, some of the sheep lose their appetites for grass and young heather shoots. Visitors feed them on everything from ham sandwiches to liquorice allsorts. They mob picnic parties, greet the arrival of every charabanc and the regular red-sided service 'buses, and have even been known to clamber into cars when doors have been left open.

Some of them sleep on the commons. Others make their way back to the hills at night but return to the village with the new dawn. Local farmers shake their heads when they see this partial disruption of the old heaf system, but there is little they can do about it, for appetite so easily over-rides instinct with these shaggy grey animals.

Matilda is a veteran – an old and tattered "Swaledale cross", thin in the wool and loose in the teeth, with tremendous curiosity and a remarkable appetite for such unsheep-like food as scones and apple peelings.

Officially, Matilda belongs to Mr. R. Smailes, of Manor House, but she has a thousand friends and spends most of her time round Goathland Church. There is a patch of ground sheltered by the Church wall that has been flattened down by Matilda and successive lambs, who have slept away the dark hours there.

Mrs. May Thompson, whose cafe is on nodding terms with the Church, said that some visitors will buy scones to feed to Matilda when photographs are being taken, and one man actually brought a baby's bottle. He figured (and rightly) that a photograph of the incident would cause a stir when he got home.

The Mallyan Hotel shrewdly had a sheep grid installed to stop Matilda and her friends entering the building. Mrs. Thompson pointed sadly to her garden, which does not boast a single flower and is merely a stretch of cropped grass. She told me that scraggy but lovable Matilda had the habit of getting in.

Once a local man dug the garden and planted it with flowers. A spring was attached to the gate. But next morning the spring was out of place and so were all the plants. There were the imprints of a sheep's feet everywhere. Matilda waits until someone arrives at the cafe and opens the garden gate. Then she shoulders her way through and makes for the kitchen door.

Mrs. Thompson continued: "Matilda knows her name. She likes to eat plums, and spits out the stones. She loves sweets. Nearly all the letters we receive from customers have the postscript 'Love to Matilda'."

There was a man from Bournemouth, however, who had a tremendous shock one morning as he was walking downstairs for his breakfast, for Matilda was on her way up. He chased her out and then went for a stroll. Looking over the Church wall, he noted an inscription of a tombstone: "Be ye also ready". This man explained that he had travelled all over the world, but Goathland was the funniest place he had known!

For several years, Matilda has given birth to her lambs in the shadow of the Church wall, and she is a proud and very capable mother. "As soon as she cleans up her lamb she brings it to the cafe gate," said Mrs. Thompson, "and then she takes it along to Mr. Smailes. She knows she belongs to him."

Matilda is not much to look at, but she has many human friends, and she must surely be the most photographed sheep on the Yorkshire moors.

"Dalesman" (1956)

Sale Time at Malham

Under the off-white amphitheatre of Malham Cove over 5,000 sheep are sold every autumn. There are five sales in all, although two of them are generally just for cattle.

The tradition of large-scale open-air bargaining goes back to the mid-eighteenth century. A Mr. Birtwhistle of Skipton made annual journeys to remote parts of Scotland, including the Hebrides, and bought black cattle. He sold them by holding a fair on Great Close, some grazing land on Malham Moor.

Later the flow of "traffic" was reversed and Scotsmen brought their sheep to a fair held nearer the village. Some 60 years ago local farmers were still gathering at the village green every October for a small fair. Lambs often sold at 7s. to 10s. each and ewes would make perhaps 15s. to 18s. apiece.

It was in 1920 that the late Mr. T.H. Taylor, a Skipton

auctioneer, launched the sales in the form that they are known today. Now they have for long been something of a tourist attraction.

Critical-eyed dealers come from as far away as Darlington and York, but the sales' roots remain firmly in Malham. They are local affairs. The farmers form a closely knit band of buyers.

A sale begins with all the farmers' names being written on pieces of paper and placed in hat. A ballot decides whose stock shall be sold first. One lot of sheep quickly follows another into the ring.

As the bidding rises dialect floats on the autumn air as farmers comment about each lot before them in unruffled tones and with a calm, almost placid manner. Time seems to come to a halt. An eyelid winks and a hundred pounds changes hands, but no voice raised in excitement interrupts the refreshing murmur of country talk or the occasional spontaneous laugh. Soon the last lot is sold and put in a wagon. It is another year before sheep attract more attention than folk at Malham.

Will Green (1965)

Tar and Grease

An old Yorkshire custom, for the passing of which no tears were shed, was the salving of sheep.

It was a custom practised before dipping became common. The farmer acquired some Stockholm tar and grease, which were heated and mixed together. Some of this mixture was applied to the skins of sheep, the wool being parted by a neat movement of the thumb and finger of the farmer.

You could always tell when a man was salving because his hands were jet black for weeks on end. It was a long and tedious job, for each animal received over a pound of salve and its application was the work of over an hour. When a flock of over a hundred sheep were being treated the farmer often hired men to help out with the work. The salve was said to be very effective whenever there was sheep-scab in the area and animals so treated were said to weather well.

Sheep-washing usually preceded clipping by a week or ten days.

A moorland stream was dammed by sods until the water was several feet deep, the sheep were then driven off the fells into a stone-walled croft near this "dub", and while one man stood in the icy water washing the sheep the other caught the animals and dropped them in to him.

Not only did this help the wool to rise and therefore make clipping easier, but it cleansed the wool of sand and grit which the animal had picked up during the preceding months on the tops.

E. Kenworthy (1964)

Counting Sheep

In certain parts of Yorkshire nearly 100 years ago the following numerals were widely used by the shepherds. From one to ten respectively we have: Yan, Tyan, Tethera, Methera, Pip, Ceser, Leser, Cathra, Horner, Dick, and from ten upwards Yanadick, Tyanadick, Tetheradick, Metheradick, Bumpit (15), Yana Bumpit, Tyana Bumpit, Tethera Bumpit, Methera Bumpit, Jiggit (20). It will be noticed that the numbers after 15 (Bumpit) are formed by the addition of those for one and two and so on, and it was a usual thing to shorten the later figures to Yanabum, Tyanabum, etc. The method of restarting from 15 is a most significant feature of the method of scoring. These numerals were fairly widely adopted to the middle of the last century, particularly through the northern counties of England and though we find many local variations in many districts yet the general likeness outweighed the difference.

This peculiar idea of sheep counting is not now in use nor has it been for some time past excepting maybe by one or two very old shepherds who have caught up the poetic jingle from their fathers. Belief that it originated from the Gaelic has been strongly contradicted by many well-known authorities who assure us that there is not the slightest attachment to this language. Comparing the numerals with those of Welsh shepherds, however, one finds a striking likeness. It is commonly believed that Welsh drovers bringing cattle and sheep into our rural markets introduced the language which was carried into the far remoteness of England's dales and vales. For a long period after this country was Anglicized Cumberland and Westmorland and other mountainous parts of the north of England were still occupied by Welsh speaking people and it is notable that these numerals are almost wholly limited to this area. It is easy therefore to imagine that Welsh-speaking British serfs, shepherding the flocks of their Saxon or Scandinavian or Norman overlords, carried on their method of counting in their mother tongue thus handing down in a rather debased form this strange language.

Dorothy Morton (1941)

Facial Cruelty

In summer the sheep were brought in for shearing and following this they were branded with the tar mark, i.e. "Spotting their jackets", but also the lambs had to face the ordeal of a burning hot iron being placed down the face from between the eyes to the tip of the nose. This blistered the flesh and burnt the black hair off, and when the new hair grew it was white, and considered more attractive to fashion. Certain branders were considered experts at the art of facial alteration.

Happily this cruel custom has almost died out. I know of no farmer who practises it to-day, but occasionally I see sheep with these markings on the face at north country auction marts.

T. C. Calvert (1946)

All We Like Sheep

They were "gathering the moors", when all the sheep were collected from the fells to be sorted and dipped. At first light the farmers went off with their dogs and their stout sticks; some had well over an hour's walk before they began their search and it was often around noon before they were back again. This was the second round-up of the year; the first was for lambing, the next would bring them down to the low pastures for the winter months.

Each man in his rough country clothing followed his quarry down the fells and along the lanes, his black and white dog padding at his heels or circling round obedient to a whistle. Before him bounced a sea of humping grey backs rippling and rolling like corn under the wind. The hooves of the sheep beat a shallow tattoo on the hard roads like a drum-stick accompaniment to his heavy footsteps.

Seen from the rear they were nothing but ragged bundles of lolloping wool; but stem that flood, face them about and then look at the assortment! For every sheep has been gathered in by the vigilant dogs regardless of owner or property. There were ewes marked with red and others with blue; some had a clear black letter stamped on their backs. Some carried bramble sprays spiked to their sides, some were hobbled, some were lame; others raced and climbed with sure-footed agility.

There were large, dreary sheep, small dapper sheep, sheep with horns and sheep without, and lambs with stubs just pushing through. There were black-faced coons and white-nosed blondes, lambs like overgrown toys on a nursery shelf, and older sheep with the dignity and bearing of a duchess. There were sheep that were frightened, angry, disdainful and curious, their fleeces hanging heavily upon them as they pattered along the lanes – fleeces grey and dun and patched with black in imitation of the limestone with which they lived.

They were a motley crowd that were shepherded into all the pastures and penfolds of the village. But they had just one thing in common – they baa'd. In every key and with every meaning they baa'd their way into each village and made the world take notice. They kept it up all day and part of the night. It was a chorus like the harmony of hounds giving tongue, or the welter of blows on an anvil.

As they poured into the villages by every route it was for all the world like the arrival of a day-trip to the sea – everyone anxious to get there first and make the most of a cheap excursion. They bumped and jostled one another, ran round, ahead and over each other; they dawdled to see all the sights and got hustled along by impatient neighbours. They moved in a mass, calling out anxiously to their families not to stray; they were on the constant search for something to eat. They bunched rather than queued to get in anywhere and all wanted to do the same thing at the same time. They were determined to see everything and miss nothing so they pushed into each gateway and round every wall. They had no compunctions about leaving litter on the roadway. They were voluble and noisy.

Like any other holiday crowd they were easily led, so, following the invitation of the busking dogs, they sought pleasure in an open doorway and flocked impetuously through. Too late, they found they were booked for a dip. There was nothing for it now but to put on a bold face and go through with it.

With startled eyes and dutch courage they fell into the pit and allowed the surge of yellow waters to cover them. Splashing and crying out with alarm, swimming a little, getting a mouthful now and then, and being blinded by the harsh sting of water on unwilling eyes, they braved it out. They kicked and floundered in the angry waves, and at last trotted out defiantly, shaking off the drips from their tossing heads. After a little lounging, and a snack or two on the sunlit grass, they streamed out once more through the wicket gate tanned a glorious golden brown. It was well to do the thing properly on a day-trip; here at last was evidence of an outing spent beneficiently in the open.

And so back to the fells. A little foot-sore and grim after the rigours of the day, they pattered their way homeward to the green slopes. It was good to be back again on the crisp hill grass by the lichened walls and the limestone boulders and with the scent of a fellside wind in one's nostrils. There had been a few minor accidents, of course, as in any holiday crowd; accommodation had been scarce and food difficult to find and children had been separated from their parents. Still, it had been a good "off" and, Yorkshirelike, they felt they had had their moneysworth.

All the same, as they cropped the short turf and bleated incessantly across the wind, there was a certain restlessness among them. They all looked to be moving about in search of something. Somehow, the fells didn't appear to be quite the same, though it was difficult to say in what way – it was as though something very familiar was missing. The ewes were vaguely distressed and wandered up and down, hoarsely complaining.

No one had thought of telling them about the Lamb Sales.

Kathleen Binns (1950)

Pig Tales

Stanley's Pigs

I don't think I ever did know Stanley's other name. He had two breeding sows, Bessie and Annie, who were litter sisters and even in maturity were near inseparable. Only when they had their own piglets, with an interval of only two days, old Stanley managed to settle them in separate pens, Bessie with 12 infants, Annie with nine.

Tuesday morning brought gales of hurricane force to Addingham Moorside, and although we had set out to the field for ploughing we were not very happy about driving under the lashing branches of the trees at the top end of the field.

Suddenly, as we came out at the bottom end, nearest the distant farm buildings, George lifted his plough and drove off on to the headland, the as yet unploughed perimeter of the field, motioning me to do the same. "What's wrong?" I shouted, above the noise of the wind. "Stanley's waving," George said briefly. Sure enough, Stanley stood up by the buildings – a solitary figure executing desperate semaphore signals which could only be translated as a cry for help.

We unhitched George's tractor. I stood on behind and we put it into top gear. As we drew nearer we could see what had happened. Although the sows with their litters were housed in separate pens, the division was a makeshift one, cutting one large wooden hut into two with a partition of corrugated sheets.

The roof was of sheets too, and the wind had lifted the front allowing the two doors which fastened on to a central wooden post to swing free, as the post tilted.

Pandemonium ensued as Bessie and Annie were rapturously reunited and 21 week-old piglets ran rings round their mothers, through the welter of mud by the cow trough. They had tipped up Stanley's wheelbarrow, frightened the life out of a hen with a brood of chickens, and put 15 pullets up in the branches of a tree.

Stanley was so hopping mad be could only splutter as we strove to corral the two happy families. Eventually we got the whole lot herded into a disused stone calf box. Only when the wild excitement of the piglets subsided and their thoughts turned to food did we at last get the right infants back to their respective parents.

Although neither sow was savage with her sister's offspring, neither would she tolerate an interloper seeking a place at her table, and a warning grunt was sufficient to send the miscreant to seek his sustenance elsewhere.

Thus, at last, two contented sows lay on their sides, nine piglets with one, 12 with the other. We let then feed and, with the minimum of fuss, persuaded Annie and her nine to take up temporary quarters in a corner of the barn, fenced off by hurdles and bales of straw.

Stanley's face shone with heat and he mopped his brow. "By gow," he said, and his tone was heartfelt, "I don't know what I'd 'a done wi'out thi."

Hazel Driver (1975)

Rodeo Time!

I waited in the car while my companion visited a friend in the village. It was quite a busy thoroughfare, but somewhere behind the houses pigs were squealing. The sound rose clearly above the noise of traffic. Five well-grown pigs, large whites, made their appearance and hustled against each other, squealing and spreading far and wide, along the road.

It was then that I became aware of a truck with trailer ramp down, which was obviously intended to take the pigs to market. Those pigs did not intend to go! Two men, brandishing sticks and their caps, were in charge of the runaways. It was some time before they managed to get the five animals collected near the vehicle.

Neighbours had come out to see the fun, for it was a regular rodeo. Five young porkers were taken by tail and ear, tugged and hustled, shouted at and sweated over, but to no avail.

The men paused to mop their brows; they listened to the advice that was being offered on all sides. Along came a newcomer, who stopped to size up the situation. He said something to one of the onlookers and in a few minutes a bucket was fetched.

Choosing the pig nearest the ramp, the newcomer clapped the pail over the pig's head. Immediately it began to move back, and with the pail held firmly over its head, and hands guiding the animal by the tail, it backed up the ramp in no time. Four more wayward pigs followed in the same way. It's easy when you know how!

"That's why ah like 'large black'," I heard one man say to another, "they've sike big lugs they carn't see we'ar tha going."

"No, by gum! But the beggars all bite yer," was the reply.

Florence Hopper (1978)

Pig Killing

Often in these days of our limited and unstable meat ration I recall pig killing day in the Yorkshire village where I spent my youth. That day was one of the few days when we did not have to provide our own entertainment, for that day always closed with a social evening and a supper.

Early on the great day grandfather would be up lighting the copper fire so that the water would be boiling before Neb the pig-sticker arrived. The arrivel of Neb was in itself a rare spectacle for he always arrived in a gaily-painted trap pulled by two milk-white horses. The trap's decorations included paintings of various breeds of pigs done by the skilled hand of a country craftsman famed for his skill in sign painting.

After the customary greetings Neb would enter the house to partake of a glass of my mother's famed gooseberry wine, whilst he exchanged local news and pondered upon childhood reminiscences with my parents. Eventually we persuaded the elders to leave their talking and precede with the business in hand.

Our cottage pig was no lean weakling, but a pig in the region of forty stone. It had to supply a large proportion of our meals for the coming twelve months. Neb had soon arranged himself in his professional clothing and armed himself with several knives of various shapes and sizes. He had now to perform the difficult task of sticking the pig, for he had no "humane killer" with which to first stun the animal.

The pig was first persuaded to stand in the region of several large sacks of straw placed to break the pig's fall, thus preventing any bruising. Then the knife fell – hard and true, and the red deluge of blood poured into the waiting bucket, it being required for the making of black pudding – a succulent and enjoyable dish.

The pig was then rolled into a tub of boiling water and the scraping began. This consisted of removing the long coarse bristles by using the sharp bases of the kitchen candlesticks.

Eventually the pig was hauled and hung on a beam, thus allowing the usual butchering arrangements to take place. After it has hung for several days, depending on the weather, the secretive and complex matter of salting took place, and even to this day I do not know what ingredients were used, although I think that vinegar, pepper and black treacle, together with a dash of rum, were placed in the long wooden troughs where the hams and sides were placed during the salting process.

But the most enjoyable time always occurred that evening of the party. What food we devoured – pork pies, sausage rolls, faggot cakes, sparry pie, scraps, fried pork cakes and many others, served with potent home-made wines, such as gooseberry, sloe, parsnip and dandelion.

After this meal the entertainment began, old ballads were sung, humorous stories were told, and two old shepherds would bring out their fiddles and we would dance well into the morning, when we would finally end by telling ghost stories. This was a very suitable type of closing for it always provided an excellent excuse for we lads to take our girl friends home.

Barrie J. Kaye (1953)

Pig and Plate

It is not only a custom but a habit for Dalesfolk when they have killed a pig to give away small portions of the pig to neighbours and friends. Few are, in fact, left out of this thoughtful interchange of gifts which has the added convenience that neighbours' pigs are usually killed at different times, therefore that tasty bit of pork, spare rib or liver is very acceptable.

The custom which, however, must prevail, is that the plate or dish upon which the gift has been made must not be washed by the recipient, but rcturncd "fully blodded". It is not deemed lucky to wash it.

R.B. Fawcett (1945)

The Squeak was Wasted!

When I was a lad, pig-killing was an exciting time, marked by the bustle and excitement of the killing, and later by the feasts of pork, pies and offal.

Sooner, or later, someone was sure to remark that "Aye! a pig's grand! We can mak use o' everry bit, bar t'bristle, an' squeak."

One day, years later, I called on Mr. Wox, the cobbler, to collect a pair of boots. He looked up from his work and remarked "I bet you never saw anybody sewing with this before."

I hadn't.

"What is it?" I asked.

"A boar's bristle," he answered, "it beats a needle everytime."

So now I know the bristle can be used, but, after 50 years, I am still waiting to hear of a use for the squeak.

Harry Herrington (1963)

The Squeak was Used!

An old gentleman who used to live near us always said at pig killing time "Everything used bar the squeal and now that's used for motor horns."

Edward Smith (1963)

Sitting wi' t' pigs

My father and I had walked over from Malham to Hellifield intending to catch a train from there to Gisburn; then walk the seven miles over Coldweather Hill to Barrowford and so home.

We arrived at Hellifield in time to see the train steaming out of the station. As we had walked a good distance that day, the prospect of having to walk all the way home was not cheerful. There was no bus service then so after some refreshment we set off hoping we might get a lift, but as it was a week-day and motorists not so numerous, we could not build on that.

It had been very cold all day and just after leaving Hellifield it began to drizzle with rain. We had walked a mile or so when a farmer's cart overtook us, and my father stopped the driver and asked if he could give us a lift. "Well," he said, "Float's full a' pigs, yo could sit here wi me, but lass 'll hev ta sit wi' t' pigs."

Riding with pigs was preferable to walking just then, so under the net I crawled. The farmer gave me a sack to cover my clothes in case any of the pigs had an 'accident'. However, the pigs were very well mannered, and after grunting a bit at being asked to squeeze up and make room for me, they were quite friendly. One of them, evidently thinking I looked more comfortable sitting in the bottom of the cart, decided to do the same, and calmly lay down beside me – her head on my feet. I was warm as a toast, and very sorry when the farmer stopped, and said our ways must part.

It needs some explanation when I tell my friends the best foot warmer I ever had was a pig's head.

Nellie Ainsworth (1946)

Haytime and Harvest

Make your hay as best you may

"To make hay while the sun shines" is a good old adage which every farmer would be glad to observe if the sun would be prepared to keep its part of the bargain. Too often in our Northern Dales the sun is slow to co-operate; it dallies too long before making its appearance, and then, when it does appear, is too restless to remain.

Just now in Yorkshire there comes that tense moment of waiting before haytime begins that is often so galling. The farmer may have his men and his machines ready and waiting day after day, with promising hay in the fields and empty barns at home. But like the wise commander of an army he has to choose the timely moment for the start of operations, and to bring all his experience to bear in the choice of that moment.

There have been years of late when the hard-bitten dalesman has changed the adage to more grim words. "Make your hay as best you may," he has said as, a few hours after he has cut and spread the hay, a storm has set him back again and he has seen haytime spread not over sunny days but over storm-ridden weeks. When labour is short and the sunny hours are few, it cannot be wondered at if at times he feels he is contending against overwhelming odds.

It is not always easy for the town-dweller to understand this attitude, because for the most part his job is not guided, controlled and ruled by the vagaries of nature. He only sees the crops in the fields – and usually only on sunny days – and the farmer gazing at them over his farm gate. He cannot easily recognise that the crop in the field is not as good as the crop in the barn. Only the man who has seen the grass grow, who has watched the daily thickening and ripening, and who can appreciate the value of what he sees – only such a person can appreciate what is at stake and the hazards that are involved in this pleasant season of haytime.

It is one thing to go out into the meadows on a summer morning, while the trees are yet wrapped in soft mist, to see the mist rise and feel the heat come, and to catch the rare elusive smell of the new-mown grass and to cry, as did one of Shakespeare's characters, "Good hay, sweet hay, hath no fellow." But it is another thing to realise that this hay is the bread and butter crop of the year, to know that upon the success or failure of its harvesting depends a large part of the food for man and beast through the long winter to come.

Haytime may be a good time or a bad time – and there is every prospect that this year's ingathering will be good – but there is too much of an element of chance about it to make it other than a time of suspense and anxiety until "all is safely gathered in."

(1949)

Sledges and Creels

Twice within the past few days I have come upon Dales' farmers devoting some of their spare time to the task of preparing their hay-sledges for use a few weeks hence, a certain portent that hay-time is imminent. This use of hay-sledges is perhaps of less note to a Yorkshireman than it would be to a southerner. In scarcely any other part of England is the device still existing as a farming implement – but presumably our Dales farmers still find it of service. To watch it in use is to see one of the last survivals of the days of a more primitive agriculture.

It is on record that Turner, the artist, in one of his Yorkshire journeys, came across a hay-sledge at work on a farm near

Rievaulx Abbey and made a sketch of it in his notebook. When later the sketch came into the possession of the National Gallery none of the authorities knew what it represented. Eventually in a catalogue it appeared as "a dismounted cart". That was a century ago, so that even then the hay-sledge must have ceased to be a common object of our countryside.

There is a particular form of hay-creel made, too, in Wensleydale, which is probably not known outside the county. It is a device of hazel rods and tarred rope and is used for carrying quantities of hay to cattle in the fields. The bulk of them are made at a one-man concern at Hawes where the dying art still lingers.

(1939)

Haytime in Raydale

Raydaleside, the valley which cradles Semerwater, has changed little since my youth of between fifty or sixty years ago. It is shorn of some of its trees, one or two modern roofs do not quite tone with the old laithes, and no longer do the roadmen sit by their heaps of stones quietly "knapping" them into the right size. Otherwise the pattern of the fields and pastures, the lake and the becks, remains much the same – but that of man's life and work has changed considerably.

In those days my arrival for haytime usually coincided roughly with that of the Irish labourers, the chief difference being that they were paid fairly well as things went, whereas my uncle usually told everyone that I could barely earn my keep!

The Irishmen worked hard, and at that time their only relaxation was on Sunday evenings, when they visited the little beer-house which Countersett then boasted, or else went down to Bainbridge.

Tractors, of course, were not even a dream, and there was much hillside meadow which the double-horse mowing machine could not touch. What a treat it was to see four or five men swinging their scythes in echelon, pausing occasionally to wet their blades, and less frequently to "wet their whistles" from the large, wicker-covered jars of beer, which it was one of my tasks to carry from the farmhouse, sometimes distances of between one and two miles. This interspersed with large baskets of food and cans of tea, which, in good hay weather, were needed from early morn until late at night.

Often my first task, well before breakfast, was "raking-off" behind the mowing-machine, which meant much plodding through wet grass. I remember a new pair of town-bought boots which turned into wet brown paper before the morning was over. A pair of clogs from Hawes proved the only solution!

Until old enough to take a turn with the men I had, perforce, to take and "dash" many odd corners, and spend hours bare-back riding with sledge-loads of hay to and from the laithes. Woe betide one if the sledge was allowed to catch a gap check through a bit of carelessness, for the crime would surely be recounted the following Sunday as we foregathered outside the old church in the fields below Stalling Busk.

Haytime progress between the opposite sides of the dale was always the subject of much banter, and those who seemed to get on quickest were accused of not getting their hay properly "made".

Given good weather haytime might be over in three or perhaps four weeks at the most, but I have known many black-looking "pikes" still standing in the fields when I returned home early in September.

Charles Carter (1959)

The Machine Age

When, many years ago, I first helped with a haytime in the Dales, someone asked me if I would like to go on the "moo". The term was so lyrical, I could not resist the job. Ten minutes later, standing on an enormous pile of hay, with my hair festooned with old cobwebs that were collected from the beams against which we eventually worked, I vowed never to take on a haytime task without full inquiries.

Those were the days when virtually every operation at hay-time was performed by hand. This year, scanning the Dales meadows, I saw few people – and a great many machines. The farmer now has a cotter-pin rather than a wisp of straw in his mouth.

Curiously, the more the job is mechanised and the less time

there seems to be for being sociable with your fellow men. When "drinkings", the haytime meal, was delivered 30 years ago, everyone broke off work, and there was talk – sometimes even song – before work resumed. Today, a terrifying momentum builds up. There is scarcely time to slake the thirst.

I know a young man who manages with only about four hours sleep in the 24 for a week or two as he "contract mows" the fields. Frequently, he turns up at a farm in time to wake up the skylark, and it may be after dark before be thinks of going home.

Meanwhile, he works by headlamp beam, travelling at some 30 miles an hour with modern flail-type mower. The old cutter machines went at little more then walking pace.

I recall a haytime when, with only an acre or two to bale, one of the tyres on the baling machine was punctured. The farmer adjusted the machine, then asked his worker to continue. And so he did with one soft tyre – until the last bale was deposited in the field by moonlight!

(1977)

Harvest Month

I was fortunate in that I was not old enough to be called up for the army until October, 1918. I went off, a strong 17 year old, to work during the summer holiday on my uncle's farm, which lay between Etton and Lockington, not far from Beverley. I had already spent holidays there and thought I knew about farm work.

In those days, every farm in that part of Yorkshire had what was called a Harvest Month, which would start on any day of the week, to be decided by the farmer, and from that day on, every day, whatever the weather, worked started at six a.m. and finished at seven p.m. with an extension to eight or later at leading time.

During this month, work was pushed on at a fast pace to make use of every bit of daylight, and any labourers living out had their mid-day meal provided by the farm. This was because only about half an hour was allowed for it, and it was brought out on fine days to where the work was going on in the field.

I was there well before the 'Month' started, and one day my

uncle said: "They have taken my horse-lad into the army; they said they would leave him until after the harvest, but he's gone. Do you think you can do his job? The foreman will come to our side of the house and knock you up in the morning."

I wondered why this was, but on the first morning I jumped out of bed at the sound of a hoe scraping on the wall below the window and found I had to go out in the half light at 4-20 a.m. to search for six horses in the horse pasture.

Tom, the foreman, and I groomed and fed them (and this we did every day for a month) until ten to six, when we went in for breakfast. At six we were all out ready to start, and a scratch crew we were, for most of the able-bodied men were by this time in the army.

That year, the harvesting on an 180 acre farm was carried out by two elderly labourers, one of them not used to farm work; a foreman somewhat younger, but exempt from the army because of a defect; an old man over seventy and myself, with my uncle and my cousin – a girl of sixteen – to feed the animals, see to the sheep, milk the cows, bring us our meals and 'lowances and changes of horses.

My first job was driving the three horses as they hauled the binder round the field, and sitting on my horse I could see the other men – apart from the foreman, who rode the binder – at their interminable work, day after day, 12 hours a day, stooking the sheaves we had thrown out.

I was happy with this arrangement, for stooking is monotonous and dreary work, but it didn't last long. When about two thirds of the corn was cut, my uncle said there was nothing else quite ripe, nor was there anything quite ready for leading to the stack-yard, for in those days all corn had to see three Sundays in the stook before it could be carted. I would have to go scruffling for a day or two. This is where my torture began.

A scruffler was a wedge-shaped iron implement standing on a couple of blades at the back and one wheel at the front, so that when it was pulled by a horse between two rows of turnips it skimmed up the weeds and loosened the soil. The operator held the reins and the handles and pulled the thing round at the turns.

Hopefully he had a horse that could walk down the rows without kicking up the turnips, and turn at the ends without getting a leg over the traces. I had one stupid old mare, Blossom by name, who could do neither. She caused me much anxiety, as did a mettlesome young one who every now and again decided that she had had enough of me, and was ready for off.

There was a change of horse three times a day, and I hated to see either of them come through the gate along with my 'lowance at nine or four o'clock. At dinner time I took my supposedly tired horse with me to join the other men. My cousin brought the food in a cart, and my fresh horse came along hitched to the back of it.

The last three hours in the afternoon, from four till seven, with a fresh horse in front of me and many miles behind me, seemed never-ending. I longed to see the stookers setting off on their way home.

My trials had only begun. After three days of this we began to lead the corn. I went with two horses and a waggon, and the labourers went with cart and horse. I thought this was unjust, but perhaps it was that it was harder to make a load on the shelvings of a cart than on a waggon. Nothing was ever explained.

Tom, the forker, was helpful. He handed me the sheaves with

the right end towards me and also the right side up. I had to place them "cockling" side upwards on the outside of the load, with perhaps two on the corners, and "cockling" side downwards for the rest, though there was much more to making a load than that. One day when one of the labourers forked me a few loads, he just slung them at me. Them I really did have to jump around.

When the load was built up until the two ends were the shape of a church window arch, the ropes were put on and off I went. On the way I had to cross a grass field which was steeply ridged. The road crossed at an angle, so that a front wheel was up when a back wheel was down. The waggon creaked and groaned, and I sat for part of each trip twisted round on the near side horse's back gazing up in an agony of apprehension at the front of the load, which any minute was going to come down, smother me, and set the horses kicking for their lives. It never did. In fact, I didn't ever have half a load "sholl" off, as one of the labourers did, and I hardly lost more than an odd sheaf.

At last, the four weeks came to an end. My uncle paid me the same as the labourers. I went home well pleased with my performance. Then I remembered the boys who left school at 14, were hired out by the year, lived in, went with horses, and before they were 16 would have had to attempt most of what I had done.

Harry Etherington (1980)

A Catchy Job

There is a tale going around the East Riding about an old farmer who, in the days when a pound was considered a farmworker's pay for week, engaged extra hands to do the stacking. Late in the afternoon, when the men were looking forward to their pay, he arrived in the "staggath" and to the disappointment of the spare hands, offered them 3s. 6d. for their day's work. One and all they refused.

One man had nothing to say, so the old farmer approached him... "Thoo'll tak 3s. 6d. is ah offer it to tha, wean't the mister?" he asked. The man said he would be delighted and took the money. "Noo, see there," the old farmer said to the lads on the stack, "yon fellow is'nt aboon takkin 3s. 6d." But he was met with a guffaw of laughter... and "We dean't wonder, he's a feller fred village, an' he's only leakin' on."

Yes, in those days work was hard and wages were small. Each farm had its Wag: its Shep: its Thoddy, and Foworthy, and Tommy Owt, and they all worked in harmony at harvest time.

It was often a catchy job, getting in the harvest, for the reaper never came out on a Sunday, and on a September morning one had to wait for the sun to come up sufficiently to "dry off" before the cutting began. Going back 100 years the school-children in the villages were given a copper or two to make straw "bands" with which the stooks were bound, but nearer our generation the reaper did that; he was followed by men who threw the stooks of corn together and left them in orderly rows to dry.

Harvest was harvest in those days. Fields with rows and rows of stooks were a picture. The wagons, painted blue, red, and yellow, collected up the heavy stooks, drawn by Blossom or Bess or Captain or Duke. The lads stuck to their corduroy trousers, despite the heat, tying them below the knee to keep out if possible the "Lousy harvest-bugs", mites which tormented any fold of the flesh for days.

There was no stripping to waist-level to enjoy the sun. The farm lads wore thick striped cotton shorts, folded back at the elbow to give their arms freedom, but only so far, for they knew what the sharp barley horns could do with their skin.

At lunch time the bairns from the farm brought lowance up. There were cans of tea, sometimes beer, hunks of bread (home-made), solid lumps of American cheese, pastries, scones, and apple pies. The baskets took some carrying. They were dumped down underneath the big chestnut tree by the gate, the reaper stopped, the horses were given their nosebags and the company sat down to enjoy the food and a pipe.

Lads on holiday from school waited about for the cutting of the last square, when the rabbits would dart and there would be a killing. For upon the "nobbling" of the poor bunnies depended that hot rabbit pie that would await the lads for supper. When swilled in a tub of water at the back door of the farm, or perhaps in the scullery, they would arrive to table in the big farmhouse kitchen, their faces aglow with sunburn and the application of common soap and hard water. They came in quietly, minus the boots they had willingly – nay, thankfully – shed in the scullery, heavy boots, despite the fact that it was high summer, twisted by toil. Each lad wore two pairs of woollen socks to protect his feet.

Leading, and the stacking, went on under a moon which looked like a huge silver cheese. The lads sang as the "shavs" were hoisted on high. The horse harness jingled as the wagons came in. The evenings and mornings were cool and the air was spicy, for it was September.

And what of today? There is no need for a Thoddy or a Foworthy. A couple of men with a combine can clear a field in a day. There is no need for old Blossom or Bess, the gay-coloured wagon rots in a corner of the field, the harvest moon comes up on bare fields disturbed only by unattractive square bundles of straw. The corn has gone, all is safely gathered in. No weary farmworkers, less toil, better wages, and yet... in missing all that work and worry of the past haven't we missed also much of the fellowship and beauty?

Florence Hopper (1969)

Ricks and Stacks

The townman almost invariably refers to "ricks" and "rickyards", while the countryman talks of "stacks" and "stackyards", with the older generation referring to "staggarths".

I lived on the Yorkshire Wolds for many years and I cannot remember hearing the word "rick" except from a "furriner", as strangers were referred to. Of course there were other names besides "stacks". Wheat used to be built into "Day Pikes". Those were round stacks containing one day's threshing. Oats and barley were usually made into "coupins", which contained enough for half day threshing. Two coupins being built end to end formed a rectangular stack.

The wheat "pikes" were built to a good height with the aid of a wooden platform on two legs called a "Monkey". This was leaned at the side and secured with ropes through the stack. The "picker", as the man was termed, stood on the platform, took the shearers as they were lifted from the wagon and lifted then on to the stack. There was always much fun "puttin' monkey up" and a good deal of banter about who was lifting most and who was slacking.

When completed a "stackprick" was pushed down the centre of the stack. On this was fitted a hood of combed straight straw, neatly cut at the top and called its "Morphin".

Then came "theaking" or thatching. On the large farms it was customary to build a row of wheat "pikes" along the road side. Great pride was taken in the building and thatching. The result was a joy to behold, each one being a replica of its neighbour perfectly built and symmetrical in every way. The coming of the combine and the Dutch barn has altered all this and the binder will soon be a "has been".

I well remember the first binder coming into the district and the hostility it aroused among the Irish harvesters who were very common in those days. The emphasis today is on speed and more speed. Why, life is lived at a speed unthought of a generation or two back, and while it is necessary to move and advance with the times in this rapidly changing world, perhaps we old ones may be excused for regretting the passing of the most colourful pictures of farming as we knew it in those bygone days.

J. Simpson (1962)

Mell Suppers

How many dalesfolk can remember when haytime was brought to a close with a mell-supper – such as they used to have in other parts of the country after the corn harvest?

The custom was recalled by a retired farmer the other day when a few of us were talking of things that once were common at haytiming.

A mell-supper was a time of revels and feasting, often out of doors, when food and drink were free to all. The younger folk danced while their elders sat round and talked or smoked and just sat. That was the hey-day of folk-dancing, and a mell-supper and the dance that followed always resulted in a new romance or two among the young people.

Mell-suppers are no more in these times, and the only lingering remnant of them is the "drinkings", which every farmer's wife is expected to provide for the field workers during haytime.

"Drinkings" usually includes food as well as liquid refreshment, and it has a utilitarian purpose in that it saves the men's time in returning to the farm when every half-hour is precious. Perhaps "drinkings" will become a "bygone" soon.

(1948)

After the Harvest

Next month Fylingdales Young Farmers' Club, and scores of people from the neighbouring villages, will crowd into the Parish Hall at Robin Hood's Bay to witness the annual Mell Supper and Barn Dance. The Hall will be decorated with sheaves of corn and turnip lanterns. Long white-clothed tables are usually laden with food, which includes the traditional "mell cake". The word "Mell" means to mix, and the cake is made up of all kinds of rich spices.

At Robin Hood's Bay everything is methodically organised by an expert committee, and the spirit of the "Harvest Home" is present. In the old days all hay and crops were cut with scythes, or "lyes". There were not self-binders and not many of the farms had reapers. The young 'uns made the bands, women tied sheaves and some would "stook" as well, and often some twenty or thirty people were seen in one field, as happy and merry as could be. Self-binders put an end to the happy army of work-folk however, and also to the fun, song and laughter which could be heard coming from every harvest field.

In those days "ten o-clocks" were sent from every farm to the field. During the "lowance" as it was called, the horses and everyone were given a spell while bread and cheese, custards, fatty cakes, tea and beer, were consumed.

A cheer would go up when the last load was tied down with ropes and set off for the stack-yard. A "mell-supper" would then be held in the large kitchen at every farm house. Long tables were set out with sirloin of beef, legs of mutton and rabbit pies, followed by a plentiful supply of plum puddings with sauce. This was followed by a cheese and any amount of ale. Song and dance commenced and went on until the early hours of the morning.

Men who had been working by piece and had been drawing so much weekly on account, were usually paid the balance at the "mell-supper", and in addition to the harvesters, the lads who had been tending stock in the lanes were also invited to the supper.

At some farms, the last sheef in a field was decorated with ribbons and called the "Mell Doll". It was placed in the middle of the big kitchen table or on the barn floor during the meal and before the dancing began.

Cyril Swales (1956)

Farming Reflections

East Riding Ways

Holderness is still the same. It must be one of the few areas in the country to resist modern villadom. Few, if any, writers have extolled its beauties, dismissing it as flat and tame, yet for those who love the rural scene Holderness has much to offer. Delightful lanes still wind to remote hamlet and outlying farm, where life meanders in peace.

Time has soldered the old farmhouse into the countryside, the ever-foraging winds have smoothed its rough walls into timelessness. There were no horses in the yards, they breed more cattle and pigs in these days, but that fierce Holderness pride in good farming is undimmed.

No witches whispered by the moss-ridden bridge, no sinister hobmen hovered by the crossroads to capture my spirit as I passed. I don't suppose anyone believes to-day that witches borrow horses for their midnight jaunts, and milk the cows on their return. Yet hard-headed though these farmers were, it was common belief among master and men that horses found sweating at their "lisks" in the morning had been witchridden. You can still see the wickenwood twigs which were pushed through the limmel-stones to "keep t' witches oot". No witch would pass these rowan twigs. Flanked by horse-shoes they made the stables doubly safe.

Actually the sweating was due to bad ventilation. In fact it was considered wise policy to "keep t' cawd oot", since warmth produced a glossy coat. One could hardly blame the stable lads for stuffing the vents with straw. In "a good spot", with dry well-roofed stables, the men spent the long winter evenings playing "merrills" and cards on the lid of the corn bin, oblivious of heat and the ammonia-ridden fug. Under these conditions "fothering up" last thing at night was easy.

These farmers and their wagoners would carry only whip-stocks of wickenwood, gads they were called. Without them crossing a ford or bridge was a hazardous affair, all water was witch territory. Crossroads, too, were awesome places. Suicides were buried there with stakes driven through their chests. These unhappy spirits, together with those of highwaymen, hanged for their multifarious sins, were reputed to wander after dark, waylaying the unwary. A wickenwood gad guaranteed safe conduct for men and horses. It is not long since vendors of farm requisites advertised them and they were always sold at fairs. Nowadays nobody queries the wood.

Sunday morning was local horse-dealing time, when the yards brimmed with horse-talk. Just as it was the custom to drink a horse's future after its first shoeing, so it was usual to "wet t' hoss's heead" after a sale. Friends, and those specially favoured, were invited into the kitchen to partake of "summat i' t' bottle", usually my grandmother's home-brewed mead or potato brandy; but strangers adjourned to the village inn.

To be asked into the kitchen was a sure sign that you had broken down the barriers. East Riding farm families still hold strong views about "makkin' free wi' strangers", but there is no doubting their hospitality if they do take you to their hearts.

Holderness farm kitchens have always been the hub of family life, the parliament, the conference room, from which emanates all policy, domestic, agricultural or personal. Life flows from there; it is the workshop of the family hive. A succession of well-fed dogs and sleek cats creep unobtrusively into the warmest spots before the blazing fire, joining the invariable gathering of tardy chicks, wrecklings and lambs brought in to share the friendly warmth beside the master's chair. The oft-scrubbed table has seen much of life, pig killings and beastings, crowdy for hens and meal for calves as well as human fare.

To sit on the oak settle is to look for the old melodeon which held pride of place on the dresser-top. On Saturday nights it would come into its own. Before potted entertainment took the field, farm families made their own. Folk from neighbouring holdings would forgather for the evening with much jesting and banter, singing and telling of tales. Sometimes tables and chairs were pushed back for a dance, but more often than not firelight flickered on a ring of spell-bound faces, while witches, ghosts and bogeys hovered in the shadows outside.

In the days of hired labour one of the lads would play the melodeon; so lurid were the ensuing tales that those who lived elsewhere were often reluctant to venture into the night. Those who lived in would scramble stocking-footed up the backstairs, the ladder-like construction leading to the "claimers" – attics. There they slept among the apples, the herbs – and often the rats and mice.

Ann Wilson (1962)

Spirit of Change

The Dales are, and should remain, essentially pastoral – 'grazier's' country, which the classic exponents of arable 'high farming' were inclined to dismiss as not truly farmed at all – but they are not a *ranch*, a stretch of virgin grassland provided by a beneficient nature to feed wide-ranging flocks and herds without any cultivation. Far from it: our meadows, our pastures from valley to hill-top, even our heather moors, and all our walls and hedges and ditches and cartways, are the product of countless generations of cultivators and improvers. Without their work – without the long history of enclosing, draining, ploughing, seeding, liming, dunging, building – the land could not carry anything like the quantity or quality of its present day stock. But cultivation and improvement are an endless task. If the land does not go forward, it will go back: and for the last fifty years or so – years of depression, rarely broken by short-lived recoveries, for the 'Cinderella of British industries' – the land, on the average, *has* gone back. Farmers and landowners alike have been forced to cut their losses, to retrench, to concentrate on what paid best in short-term, to 'cash in' on present, and to neglect future fertility. Small wonder that the shrewd speculative 'dealer-farmer', spending his time and energy in following the markets, and using his farm as a mere harbourage for a floating population of stock, has become pronounced Dales type.

All this must change – is, in fact, already changing under the exigencies of war. Farmers must spend less time at market and more time in their fields. Short-term, hand-to-mouth, 'bargain' profits (usually involving someone else's loss) must give place to long-term, secure prosperity based on a progressive up-grading of the land, with correspondingly larger and finer flocks and herds, and correspondingly increased output. There will be many 'snags' and no success without hard thinking and hard work. Long effort will be needed to find, to keep and to use more workers, more capital, more organization, more brains and, above all, the experimenting, enterprising, fighting spirit of an expanding industry. But I've no doubt it can be done.

John Dower (1942)

The Sweat of Our Brows

We townsmen may love the Dales and know their wonderful ins and outs and ups and downs more extensively than a genuine dalesman. In our youth we may tramp the length and breadth of them, in gangs or singly according to preference, breathing great gulps of rare Pennine air into our lungs to carry back with us to the prison-house. In middle age we may – God forgive us! – shoot through them in motorcars every weekend. In old age we may hope to retire to some remote cottage, where, by walking humbly in the way of the dalesfolk, we may learn to kid ourselves that we really belong. But we never do belong. We are always visitors – unless we have been made free of the Dales by the sweat of our brows.

My friend, George Alderson, cobbler, of Gunnerside, has rarely left his native village in all his eighty-eight years. He has been too busy with the business of the Dales to know much about them, and by that very fact he is part of them. To this day I know little of Nidderdale, for I certainly had no leisure to explore it then and the very thought of revisiting it has always made my back ache. But for seven days I was part of it, and that's something for a townsman to be mighty proud of all his life.

Yes, in that memorable week I learned at first hand more than most people know about the processes of:

1.	Cuttin'	5.	Pikin'
2.	Turnin'	6.	Forkin'
3.	Nag-rakin'	7.	Stackin'
4.	Sammin'	8.	Mewin'

There was one great day when six of us succeeded in clearing a seven-acre field – cut, sammed, raked, turned, forked, and finally safely mewed in a barn, all between 4 a.m. and 9-30 p.m., without any break for meals. Good going that, and only possible under the most unrelenting fierce sun!

But pride and shame are inextricably mingled. I have to confess by ignomonious failure to handle any tool effectively. I began with a fork, pitching hay from pike to cart. I thought I was doing tolerable well until the farmer came along and gave me his views. He proceeded to demonstrate, forking up in one jab more hay than I had managed in a dozen. "*Them's* forkfuls!" he explained. I never got the trick of it. I kept falling over the nag-rake. I slid off the broad back of a horse as it climbed a hill as steep as a farm-house roof. Finally, while we were chucking huge flat stones to each other, stones that were to be the foundation of a stack, I stooped at the wrong moment, caught a stone on my forehead, and was laid out. I bear the scar to this day.

Only once did I come anywhere near shining. We were out on the high road with gripes, dipping stones out of the bank. My friend made some unkind remark about my progress. "Nay, leave 'im be," said the farmer, "'e 'andles gripe better nor 'e 'andles fork!"

My hands were a mass of burst blisters, my whole body ached as it never ached before or since. I became shameless. I got into the way of sneaking behind a wall at every opportunity to swig at a bottle of home-brewed ale – "yoll", the farmer called it. I ate like a pig, and was in a furious temper with everybody, including myself. To cap all, I found at the end of the week I was not to be paid one penny piece for all my agonies, physical and mental.

Gordon Stowell (1941)

The Loneliness of the Fields

We ruralists are losing our individuality and all that made us a race apart. That race was perhaps a bit slower of thought and movement, more conservative, content with simpler things but was made up of robust men and women, with brawn and muscle, sturdy, staid and dependable, proud and independent.

They lived the true communal life of mutual assistance expected, given and reciprocated in emergency, or occasions when every hand counted at such "throng times" as hay-time, corn harvest, threshing and sheep-clipping days, and, of course, the "boon" ploughing-days. The latter was the friendly welcome given to a newcomer to the farming ranks of any area. All those tilling land in the parish fixed a day on which they would send ploughs, men and horses to plough for him the biggest arable field on his holding. The horses vie with each other in grooming, in rosettes and, of course, glittering horse-brasses, now so much sought after by collectors that Birmingham sends out cheap imitations.

In the era of which I speak there were from a dozen to a score, men, women and children, working in hay and corn fields. From them came song and laughter. The plough-boy whistled as he followed the horses he loved, and guided them and the plough so that his furrows were so straight that he was proud of them and unafraid of the critical eye of the bands of youths. They, on a Sunday afternoon, toured the parish to inspect ploughing and the thatching of stacks together with the home-made ornaments which surmounted them for decoration.

Today, the loneliness of the fields, the absence of the bands of workers, of their music, laughter and banter, and the absence of horses, are all sadly impressive. The soul seems to have been dragged out of it all.

J. Fairfax-Blakeborough (1969)

DALESMAN